WIND EFFECTS ON BUILDINGS
Volume 2

Statistics and Meteorology

WIND EFFECTS ON BUILDINGS

Volume 2

Statistics and Meteorology

T. V. LAWSON

D.I.C., B.Sc., F.R.Ae.S., F.R.Met.S.

Reader in Industrial Aerodynamics,
Department of Aeronautical Engineering,
University of Bristol, Bristol, UK

APPLIED SCIENCE PUBLISHERS LTD
LONDON

APPLIED SCIENCE PUBLISHERS LTD
RIPPLE ROAD, BARKING, ESSEX, ENGLAND

British Library Cataloguing in Publication Data

Lawson, T. V.
    Wind effects on buildings.
    2: Statistics and meteorology
    1. Wind-pressure
    I. Title
    624'.176   TA654.5

ISBN 0-85334-893-6

WITH 3 TABLES AND 54 ILLUSTRATIONS
© APPLIED SCIENCE PUBLISHERS LTD 1980

Printed in Great Britain by Galliard (Printers) Ltd, Great Yarmouth

Preface

'Wind Effects on Buildings' has been written both for the academic and the practitioner in the design of buildings, be he architect or engineer. The theoretical and experimental aspects are described in Volume 1 where the use of statistics and meteorology has proved necessary. To allow the smooth flow of the aerodynamic arguments without breaks, in which the derivation of statistical or meteorological expressions is demonstrated, the work is presented in two volumes. This volume contains the derivation of statistical and meteorological expressions required in the companion volume.

It was realised that statistical analysis (and, to a lesser extent, meteorology) plays an ever-increasing part in all branches of engineering and design and that while most textbooks on statistics are written for the student of that subject, very few cater for the user. The presentation in this volume is designed for the user of Volume 1 and, with very little alteration, it has been extended to help those in all branches of engineering and design, whose needs are very similar. It is hoped, therefore, that Volume 2 by itself will prove useful to many readers who have no occasion to use Volume 1.

I would like to acknowledge the very considerable assistance I have received from Nick Cook, Ian Harris and John Mayne, whose numerous comments on the first draft of this volume have been incorporated to the advantage of the volume.

Contents

1

Statistics: Introduction

In Volume 1 it was found necessary to use statistics to quantify certain variables. Rather than break off in the middle of an argument to explain the statistical derivation, it was decided to combine all the statistical explanations together with some basic ideas about meteorology in a separate text: Volume 2.

Many textbooks on statistics are written for the student of statistics and start with definitions of a range of terms such as ergodic, deterministic, stationary, etc. In this text, which is written for practising engineers to understand the contents of Volume 1, the approach is inverted. Here an attempt is made to develop the arguments *ab initio*, explanations appearing in the text and definitions being restricted to the end of the chapter (Section 1.11). When a term is explained in that paragraph, it will be marked with a dagger in the text.

Throughout this text the quantity being measured will be called 'windspeed'; exactly the same techniques could be applied if the quantity were pressure, force, deflection, acceleration, etc. The next nine sections concern themselves with measurements at one point in space, and Section 1.10 deals with measurements at two points in space.

1.1. Time-invariant Windspeed

In an ideal world the windspeed would have a unique value which can be determined without the use of statistics. Due either to possible errors by the experimenter or to a lack of precision in the instruments used, it is not unknown for the same windspeed to be measured many times and the answers to be different. The ideas of statistics can be applied to these readings to produce a 'best answer' or to produce a range of values with a stated confidence that the true value is within the range. This technique is well known and will not be considered further in this volume. For this topic the reader is referred to a book on instrumentation, such as Brinkworth [4] or Ower and Pankhurst [36].

1.2. TIME-VARYING WINDSPEED

Two subdivisions of this type of variation are apparent: the variation can be deterministic (as in Fig. 1.1) or random (as in Fig. 1.2).

1.3. DETERMINISTIC FLUCTUATING WINDSPEED

The simplest form of a periodic fluctuating windspeed is shown in Fig. 1.1(a), in which the amplitude is constant with respect to time and there is a single frequency present. This windspeed can be expressed analytically:

$$u(t) = a \sin \omega t \tag{1.1}$$

A more complex variation can be envisaged in which the windspeed is compounded of two constant-amplitude fluctuations of different frequencies. This would be expressed as

$$u(t) = a_1 \sin \omega_1 t + a_2 \sin (\omega_2 t + \varepsilon) \tag{1.2}$$

More complexity can be achieved by the addition of extra terms, as in

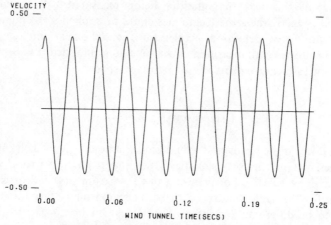

Fig. 1.1(a). Deterministic variable $V = An \sin \omega t$.

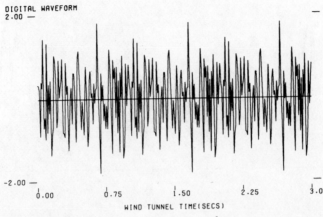

FREQS 5 9 11 15 17 23 30 38 47 52

Fig. 1.1(b). Deterministic variable $V = \sum\limits_{i=1}^{s} A_i \sin(\omega_i t + \phi_i)$.

Fig. 1.1(b). Meanwhile, a different form of a deterministic fluctuating windspeed could be produced if the amplitude varied with time in a known fashion:

$$u(t) = a(t) \sin \omega t \qquad (1.3)$$

where $a(t)$ is a known function of time.

Each of the terms in eqn. (1.2) can be of this form, but the windspeed so defined is deterministic because at any given instant its value at any past or future time can be determined.

Statistics are not used to express this type of variation.

1.4. RANDOM FLUCTUATING WINDSPEED

The windspeed in the atmosphere varies, in a fashion similar to that depicted in Fig. 1.2. It is impossible to express this variation quantitatively by an equation such as eqn. (1.2), even if the coefficients are functions of time as in eqn. (1.3), because the future behaviour is unknown and cannot be predicted. In this case a quantitative assessment can be made, either by studying a sample and extracting a value for a specific instant, say the maximum value in the sample, or by trying to define the whole sample in statistical terms.

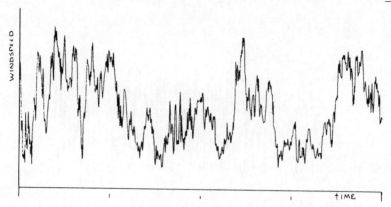

Fig. 1.2. Random variable.

1.5. Summary of Relationships

For reasons which will become clear when correlations are discussed, it is convenient to split the time-varying windspeed $V(t)$ into a mean $(\bar{U})$ and a fluctuating $(u(t))$ part. This is illustrated in Fig. 1.3 and is defined by eqn. (1.4). To save writing time throughout this volume, the windspeed $V(t)$ will hereafter be written V. Thus

$$V = \bar{U} + u(t) \tag{1.4}$$

The term 'mean' denotes an average over a time interval and for some variables the mean value tends to a constant as the averaging time is increased. In the case of the windspeed used to illustrate the operations in these chapters this does not happen, and it is conventional to define a mean windspeed as the average over one hour. This averaging time is chosen for two reasons.

(i)   There is little energy in the natural wind with a frequency of $1/3600$ Hz, as this frequency falls between the higher frequencies produced in the form of turbulence by the passage of the wind over the ground and the lower frequencies of weather systems (see the 'spectral gap' in the introduction to Chapter 9).

(ii) The eddy sizes associated with this averaging time are extremely large compared to the size of the buildings and their wakes, in which we are interested.

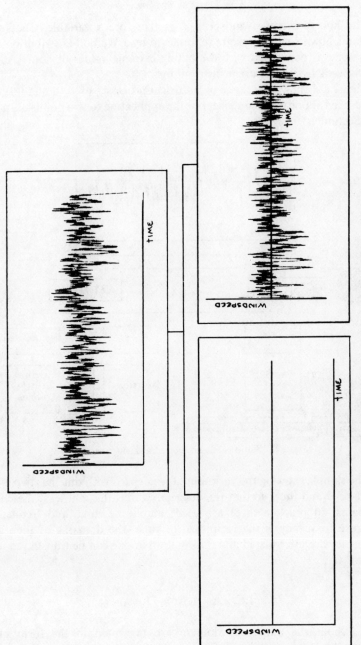

Fig. 1.3. Separation of windspeed into mean and fluctuating parts.

The hourly average windspeed $\bar{U}$ is therefore a variable. Chapter 9 explains how its variations are represented by a Weibull Distribution and Chapter 5 is concerned with evaluating extreme values of hourly mean windspeeds from the parent distributions.

Figure 1.4 shows the range of statistical processes used to quantify the windspeed at one point in space. For the application to two points in space, see Section 1.10.

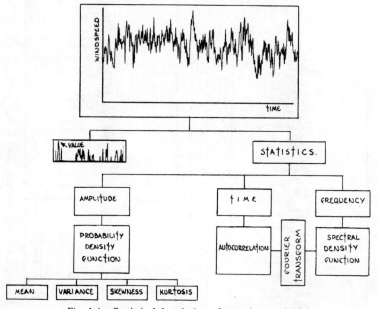

Fig. 1.4. Statistical description of a random variable.

The sample showing the variation of windspeed with time has two axes, windspeed and time, so that the description must have at least these two domains. In practice three are used: amplitude, time and frequency. Because frequency is the reciprocal of time, the domains of time and frequency are interrelated and information in one can be transferred into the other.

1.6. AMPLITUDE DOMAIN

Data about the amplitude domain are presented in the form of a 'probability density function'. Consider the sample of windspeed shown in

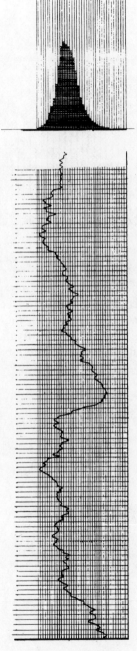

Fig. 1.5. Estimation of amplitude of windspeed.

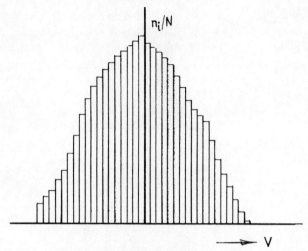

Fig. 1.6. Amplitude histogram of windspeed.

Fig. 1.5. Its magnitude is measured at regular intervals along the trace. The amplitude scale is divided into a number of cells, and each time the measurement is within the limits of the cell the tally of the number of readings within that cell is increased by one. By the time the whole sample has been studied, each cell will contain the number of instances when the

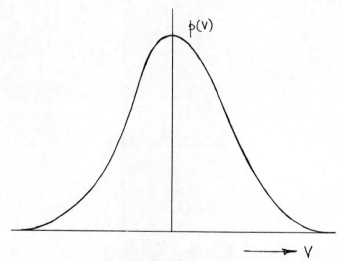

Fig. 1.7. Probability density function for windspeed.

magnitude of the windspeed was within the limits of the cell, as in the right-hand side of Fig. 1.5. When the number of readings in each cell is divided by the total number of readings, a histogram can be drawn as in Fig. 1.6. If the individual cells are reduced to zero width, a smooth curve is produced as in Fig. 1.7 and the abscissa, which was n_i/N, is now called the 'probability density function' $p(V)$.

Because of its derivation, it follows that

$$\int_{-\infty}^{\infty} p(V)\,\mathrm{d}V = 1 \tag{1.5}$$

The process of integration can be taken a step further; the first moment of $p(V)$ is equal to the mean value

$$\int_{-\infty}^{\infty} Vp(V)\,\mathrm{d}V = \int_{-\infty}^{\infty} [\bar{U} + u(t)]p(V)\,\mathrm{d}V = \bar{U} \tag{1.6}$$

and the second moment is equal to the mean square value

$$\int_{-\infty}^{\infty} V^2 p(V)\,\mathrm{d}V = \Phi^2 \tag{1.7}$$

As mentioned earlier, it is often useful to subtract the mean value from all readings so that eqns. (1.6) and (1.7) become

$$\int_{-\infty}^{\infty} u(t)p(V)\,\mathrm{d}V = 0 \tag{1.8}$$

and

$$\int_{-\infty}^{\infty} u^2(t)p(V)\,\mathrm{d}V = \sigma_u^2 \tag{1.9}$$

where σ^2 is called the *variance* and its positive square root is called the *standard deviation*.

By combining eqns. 1.7 and 1.9, the variance, the mean value and the mean square value can be shown to be related by the expression

$$\sigma_u^2 + \bar{U}^2 = \Phi^2 \tag{1.10}$$

The next two moments are used, but are only related to the fluctuating part and are always made non-dimensional by dividing by the cube and fourth power of the standard deviation respectively. Thus

$$\text{skewness} = \frac{1}{\sigma^3} \int_{-\infty}^{\infty} u^3(t)p(V)\,\mathrm{d}V \tag{1.11}$$

and

$$\text{kurtosis} = \frac{1}{\sigma^4} \int_{-\infty}^{\infty} u^4(t) p(V) \, dV \qquad (1.12)$$

These terms are discussed further in Chapter 2.

If the windspeed were the cumulative result of a large number of different actions without any restraints being placed upon any of its constituents, the probability density function would follow the 'normal' or 'Gaussian' distribution (see Section 2.5 for a fuller explanation of a Gaussian process. Windspeed, incidentally, is not Gaussian but the term windspeed has been used here as a typical variable) which is given as

$$p(V) = (1/\sqrt{2\pi}) \exp\left[-u^2(t)/2\sigma_u^2 \right] \qquad (1.13)$$

Sometimes the windspeed is composed of several components, each of which is the result of a large number of unrestrained motions; in this case the distribution has a form different from that in eqn. (1.13). Many distributions have been identified as approximations to known types of occurrence; in other instances the distribution of experimental data follows no known shape and the results must be presented graphically.

The probability density function is considered at length in Chapter 2.

1.7. TIME DOMAIN

It is more difficult to decide how time can best be presented and the way found convenient is to produce correlations. In Fig. 1.8 the same sample of windspeed is drawn twice, with the lower trace displaced by time τ. The two instantaneous values of windspeed, one at time t and the other at time $(t + \tau)$, are then multiplied together, the product being computed for the whole sample. The mean value of this product over the whole sample is called the autocorrelation:

$$R(\tau) = \overline{[\bar{U} + u(t)][\bar{U} + u(t + \tau)]} \qquad (1.14)$$

When the mean value has been subtracted from all readings the quantity is called the autocovariance:

$$C(\tau) = \overline{u(t)u(t + \tau)} \qquad (1.15)$$

This has units of velocity squared. A non-dimensional autocovariance coefficient $c(\tau)$ can be produced by dividing by the variance

$$c(\tau) = C(\tau)/\sigma_u^2 = \overline{u(t)u(t + \tau)}/\overline{u^2(t)} \qquad (1.16)$$

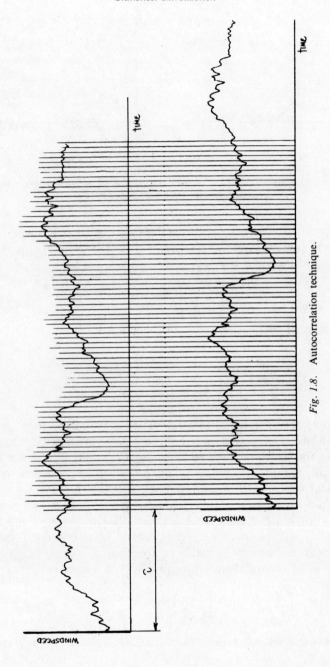

Fig. 1.8. Autocorrelation technique.

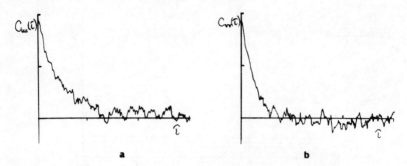

Fig. 1.9. Autocovariance function for two components of windspeed: (a) along-wind
component; (b) cross-wind component.

and a typical variation of $c(\tau)$ with τ is shown in Fig. 1.9. The integration of
$c(\tau)$ with respect to τ gives a single value of time associated with the sample.
This is called the integral time:

$$T = \int_0^\infty c(\tau)\, d\tau \qquad (1.17)$$

All forms of correlations and covariances are considered further in
Chapter 5.

1.8. FREQUENCY DOMAIN

The sample of windspeed in Fig. 1.2 related amplitude to time, and the
amplitude and time domains have been considered in Sections 1.6 and 1.7.
However, the structural engineer designing the buildings which respond
dynamically to the wind excitations finds it much more convenient to work
in terms of mode shapes and frequencies. It is therefore simpler for the
overall study to express the windspeed also in terms of frequency (which is
the reciprocal of time), rather than in time itself. Obviously, no additional
information will be produced: it is simply transformed so that its
implications can then more readily be appreciated.

A one-sided spectral density function $S(n)^*$ is defined such that

$$\int_0^\infty S(n)\, dn = \sigma^2 \qquad (1.18)$$

---

* A two-sided spectral density function $G(n)$ is sometimes used in which $\int_{-\infty}^\infty G_{uu}(n)\, dn = \sigma_u^2$.

and this function is related to the autocovariance by the Fourier transformation

$$S(n) = 4 \int_0^\infty C(\tau) \cos 2\pi n\tau \, d\tau \tag{1.19}$$

Because the autocovariance is symmetrical, the spectral density function is real after performing this transformation. The inverse relationship, i.e.

$$C(\tau) = \int_0^\infty S(n) \cos 2\pi n\tau \, dn \tag{1.20}$$

also exists. Because of its definition $S(n)\delta n$ represents the contribution to σ^2 in the frequency range n to $(n + \delta n)$. This aspect was originally studied with respect to electrical transmission theory, and the term 'power spectrum' was coined and still tends to linger; the reference to power in the wind context is misleading and the term 'spectral density function', or 'spectrum' for short, will be used in these volumes. Spectra are discussed in Chapter 3.

1.9. SIMULTANEOUS TREATMENT OF TWO COMPONENTS OF WINDSPEED

Some properties, and windspeed is one of them, are further complicated because they can be split into components. Thus

$$V^2 = [\bar{U} + u(t)]^2 + v^2(t) + w^2(t) \tag{1.21}$$

The top part of Fig. 1.10 repeats Fig. 1.4 but applies to the $u(t)$ component; the bottom part is similar and applies to the $v(t)$ component (right hand side). Between the two parts, the interactions between the components are considered.

In the amplitude domain the interaction is expressed as a covariance function:

$$\sigma_{uv}^2 = \overline{u(t)v(t)} \tag{1.22}$$

and, as with the autocovariance function of eqn. (1.15), it is often convenient to express this as a covariance coefficient function

$$c_{uv}(0) = \overline{u(t)v(t)}/\sigma_u \sigma_v \tag{1.23}$$

In the time domain the autocovariance function becomes a cross covariance function

$$C_{uv}(\tau) = \overline{u(t)v(t + \tau)} \tag{1.24}$$

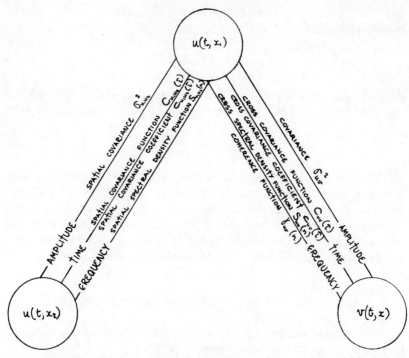

Fig. 1.10. Simultaneous statistical descriptions of two random variables.

but in this case the function is not symmetric about $\tau = 0$, and the whole range $-\infty < \tau < +\infty$ must be examined. Again, this is usually expressed in coefficient form by dividing by the standard deviation of u and v separately:

$$c_{uv}(\tau) = \overline{u(t)v(t + \tau)}/\sigma_u \sigma_v \qquad (1.24a)$$

On transformation to the frequency domain the unsymmetric behaviour has further repercussions and the spectral density function becomes complex. This can be separated into an in-phase or real part (often called a cospectrum P) and a quadrature or imaginary part which is $\pi/2$ out of phase (often called the quadspectrum Q).

Thus

$$S_{uv}(n) = 2 \int_{-\infty}^{\infty} C_{uv}(\tau) \exp(-i2\pi n\tau) \, d\tau$$

$$= P_{uv}(n) - iQ_{uv}(n) \qquad (1.25)$$

and the inverse function

$$C_{uv}(\tau) = \int_0^\infty [P_{uv}(n)\cos 2\pi n\tau + Q_{uv}(n)\sin 2\pi n\tau]\,dn \qquad (1.26)$$

Sometimes the complex spectrum is presented as a modulus and a phase angle:

$$S_{uv}(n) = |S_{uv}(n)|\exp[-i\theta_{uv}(n)] \qquad (1.27)$$

where

$$|S_{uv}(n)| = [P_{uv}^2(n) + Q_{uv}^2(n)]^{1/2} \qquad (1.28)$$

and

$$\theta_{uv}(n) = \tan^{-1}[Q_{uv}(n)/P_{uv}(n)] \qquad (1.29)$$

1.10. Measurements at Two Points in Space

Sections 1.1 to 1.9 have been concerned with values at one point in space; Sections 1.4 to 1.8 related to either the windspeed or to one of its components. The presentation of data on the inter-relation of two components of windspeed was discussed in Section 1.9. In this section the interrelation of the same parameter, but at two different points in space, is discussed. For clarity the parameter discussed will again be the windspeed. These relationships are shown on the left hand side of Fig. 1.10 where the u-component of windspeed at a location at the top of the figure is related to the u-component of windspeed at a different location on the bottom left hand side of the figure.

In the amplitude domain the variance function is replaced by the spatial covariance function

$$C_{uu}(r, r') = \overline{u(r,t)u(r',t)} \qquad (1.30)$$

In Section 1.7 it was explained how an integral time was derived; in two-point studies a similar technique is used to produce integral length scales

$$^uL_r = \int_{-\infty}^\infty c_{uu}(r, r + \delta r)\,d(\delta r) \qquad (1.31)$$

where

$$c_{uu}(r, r + \delta r) = \overline{u(r,t)u(r+\delta r,t)}/[\overline{u^2(r,t)}\ \overline{u^2(r+\delta r,t)}]^{1/2}$$

With windspeed there are nine integral length scales for the three coefficients of windspeed (u, v and w) in the three components of r (x, y and z).

In the time domain, the relevant function is the cross covariance function defined as

$$C_{uu}(r, r', \tau) = \overline{u(r, t)u(r', t + \tau)} \qquad (1.32)$$

which transforms into the cross spectral density function $S_{uu}(r, r', n)$ in the frequency domain. Due to the asymmetry of the spatial covariance function, the cross spectral density function is again complex, having a real (cross cospectral density function $P_{uu}(n)$) and an imaginary (cross quadspectral density function $Q_{uu}(n)$) part. A phase angle is the ratio of imaginary to real part.

A coherence function is now defined as

$$\gamma_{uu}^2(r, r', n) = |S_{uu}(r, r', n)|/[S_{uu}(r, n)S_{uu}(r', n)]^{1/2} \qquad (1.33)$$

1.11. DEFINITIONS

A *deterministic* variable is one whose known value at any given instant of time (epoch) will determine the value at any other past or future epoch. It can be either periodic or non-periodic (sometimes called transient). The periodic variable can be sinusoidal, complex-periodic or almost-periodic. The difference between the last two is that, although the variable in both cases is composed of a number of sinusoidal frequencies, the individual values of the frequencies in the almost-periodic are such that the periodic time (the time for the process to repeat itself) tends to infinity.

A *random* variable is one whose known value at any given epoch does not determine the value at any other past or future epoch. It can either be stationary or non-stationary. A series of samples are taken of a variable and the mean value and autocorrelation function are calculated from the values at a given interval t from the beginning of each sample. When the mean value and autocorrelation function are the same when calculated for all values of t, the variable is said to be '*weakly stationary*'. When all the moments of the probability function are also constant for all values of t, the variable is said to be '*strongly stationary*'.

A stationary variable is called '*ergodic*' when the mean value and autocorrelation function calculated as averages over a single sample are equal to the values calculated from the ensemble of samples.

In practice, a critical sample length in the investigation of a random process is defined such that the calculation of mean value and autocorrelation function are unaltered by increasing the length of the sample above that length. The critical length is called the '*stationary length*'.

Values derived from one sample of length greater that the stationary length are loosely said to have been derived from a stationary sample and this is the requirement usually assumed in Volume 1 of this work.

Thus the results from a stationary sample depend only upon the difference in time between readings, and not upon the absolute time at which the reading was taken. A stationary process is *homogeneous* if the results are independent of their space locations and only depend upon their spatial separation in a fixed direction. If, in addition to being stationary and homogeneous, the results depend only upon their spatial separation irrespective of direction, the process is called *isotropic*.

The design process is often involved with extreme values. If a number of samples, each of a length greater than the stationary length, are measured, then the mean value and autocorrelation functions of each sample would be the same. The maximum or extreme value in each sample, however, would be different and, in general, the greater the total sample length, the greater would be the largest value in the sample. A special branch of statistics dealing with extreme values has been developed and the highlights are presented in Chapter 5.

2

Statistics: Probability Density Function

Chapter 1 introduced the application of statistics to measurement with a fairly broad-brush treatment. In Section 1.6 the probability density function was shown to be the best method by which to quantify amplitude measurements. Section 1.6 went on to define the first four moments of the probability density function (eqns. (1.6), (1.9), (1.11) and (1.12)) which produce numerical values with which to describe certain aspects of the amplitude.

In this chapter these concepts are enlarged and a series of special probability density functions and cumulative distribution functions which have relevance to problems in volume 1 are detailed.

The subject of joint probability is then introduced in Section 2.15. This concept is required when the property under consideration is a function of two variables which can vary independently—for example, the pressure on the surface of a building is a function of pressure coefficient and windspeed, both of which vary with time and have their own probability density function.

2.1. MOMENTS OF THE PROBABILITY DENSITY FUNCTION

It was explained in Chapter 1 that the first four moments of the probability density function produce numerical values which quantify various aspects of the amplitude of the windspeed. These are repeated for the windspeed defined by eqn. (1.4).

By definition:

$$\int_{-\infty}^{\infty} p(V)\,\mathrm{d}V = 1 \tag{2.1}$$

18

first moment:

$$\int_{-\infty}^{\infty} V p(V) \, dV = \bar{U} \qquad (2.2)$$

second moment:

$$\int_{-\infty}^{\infty} u(t) p(V) \, dV = \sigma_u^2 \qquad (2.3)$$

Two new terms are defined: 'skewness' and 'kurtosis'. These are non-dimensional forms of the third and fourth moments respectively. Thus

$$\text{skewness} = (1/\sigma_u^3) \int_{-\infty}^{\infty} u^3(t) p(V) \, dV \qquad (2.4)$$

$$\text{kurtosis} = (1/\sigma_u^4) \int_{-\infty}^{\infty} u^4(t) p(V) \, dV \qquad (2.5)$$

The mean value $\bar{U}$ and its use are obvious. The variance σ_u^2 and its positive square root, the standard deviation σ_u, are similar to the mean

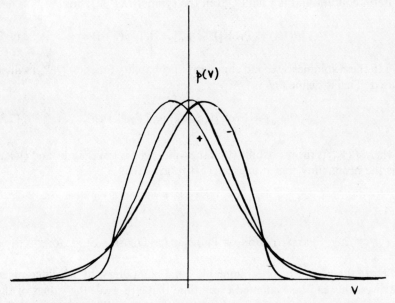

Fig. 2.1. Probability density functions showing positive and negative skewness.

square (Φ^2) and root mean square (Φ) values except that they have had the mean value removed. Thus, by eqns. (1.7) and (2.3),

$$\Phi^2 = \bar{U}^2 + \sigma_u^2 \tag{2.6}$$

The skewness is a measure of the symmetry of the probability density function. When skewness is zero, the function is symmetric about the mean value. Positive and negative skewness are illustrated in Fig. 2.1.

Owing to the fourth power involved, the value of kurtosis is heavily weighted towards the values in the tails of the distribution. For a sample which has a Gaussian distribution, the value of kurtosis is 3. If a higher value occurs, it signifies that there are either a few very large readings present or a larger number than in a sample which follows a Gaussian distribution of fairly large values. The former cause can sometimes represent 'fall-outs' in the instrumentation system.

2.2. CUMULATIVE DISTRIBUTION FUNCTION

In many studies the design value is defined as the value which has a stated probability of being exceeded. Thus a cumulative distribution function is a useful concept and is usually given the symbol $P(V_0)$. Thus

$$P(V_0) = \text{Prob}\,[V < V_0] = \int_{-\infty}^{V_0} p(V)\,\mathrm{d}V \tag{2.7}$$

In these volumes a second cumulative probability function $Q(V_0)$ will be used. This is defined as

$$Q(V_0) = \text{Prob}\,[V > V_0] = \int_{V_0}^{\infty} p(V)\,\mathrm{d}V \tag{2.8}$$

where $P(V_0)$ is the probability that the windspeed is less than V_0 and $Q(V_0)$ is the probability that it is greater. It follows that

$$P(V_0) + Q(V_0) = 1 \tag{2.9}$$

2.3. PRESENTATION OF PROBABILITY DENSITY FUNCTIONS

Before the advent of programmable hand computers, by which complex expressions can be evaluated every time they are used, the values of the functions were presented in tabular form and this is still commonplace. But it would be impossible to present tables covering distributions which have different mean values and variance. For some distributions a universal form can be derived if the variable is changed to include the mean value and standard deviation. For a sample which follows a Gaussian distribution, described in Section 2.5, if a new function z is defined as

$$z = (V - \bar{U})/\sigma_u = u(t)/\sigma_u \qquad (2.10)$$

then the probability density function of the variable z is easy to tabulate. The expression is given in eqn. (2.13).

For the rest of this chapter the variable will be called x or y if it is general, and z if it satisfies eqn. (2.10) and has a zero mean and unit standard deviation. This will facilitate the derivation of the probability density function of a new variable related to the first whose probability density function is known. The function x, y or z will be defined immediately below the equation representing the function.

2.4. TRANSFORMATION OF VARIABLES IN DISTRIBUTIONS

When the variable x has a known probability density function $p(x)$, and a new variable y can be produced which is related to x by the relationship

$$y = f(x)$$

then, providing that relationship is monotonic, the probability density function $p(y)$ of variable y can be obtained by equating the area under the original probability density function curve between the limits x_1 and x_2, with the area under the new probability density function curve between the limits y_1 and y_2 where $y_1 = f(x_1)$ and $y_2 = f(x_2)$.

In mathematical terms this relationship can be written

$$p(x)\,dx = p(y)\,dy$$

or more accurately

$$p(y) = p(x)|dx/dy| \qquad (2.11)$$

2.5. GAUSSIAN DISTRIBUTION

When a sample of data on windspeed is composed of a very large number of different motions, each of which can be described by its own probability

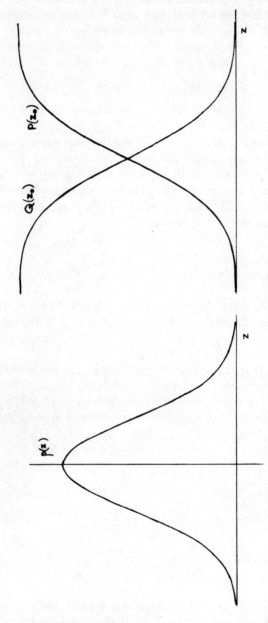

Fig. 2.2. Probability density function and cumulative distribution function for a Gaussian distribution.

density function, then the central limit theorem shows that the composite variable will follow a Gaussian distribution whose probability density function is given by

$$p(x) = (1/\sqrt{2\pi}\sigma_x)\exp\left[-(x-\bar{x})^2/2\sigma_x^2\right] \tag{2.12}$$

When $x = \bar{U} + u(t)$ this represents the windspeed.

It was suggested in Section 2.3 that tabulation of the Gaussian distribution would be simplified if it were presented in the form of the variable z, related to $u(t)$ by eqn. (2.10):

$$z = (x - \bar{x})/\sigma_x$$

$$dz = dx/\sigma_x \quad \text{or} \quad dx/dz = \sigma_x$$

$$p(z) = p(x)|dx/dz|$$

$$= \exp\left[-z^2/2\right]/(2\pi)^{1/2} \tag{2.13}$$

where $z = u(t)/\sigma_u$.

The cumulative distribution for the Gaussian distribution is given by

$$P(z_0) = (1/\sqrt{2\pi})\int_{-\infty}^{z_0} \exp\left[-z^2/2\right]dz = 1 - Q(z_0)$$

which cannot be integrated in closed form. Tabulated values for $P(z_0)$ and $Q(z_0)$ occur in many books, for instance Abramowitz and Stegun [2]. The advent of the programmable hand calculator has introduced the need occasionally to calculate the cumulative distribution function in the middle of another calculation, and for this the series expansion given as eqn. (26.2.17) in Abramowitz and Stegun [2] can be used.

The variations of $p(z)$ and $P(z)$ with z for the Gaussian distribution are shown in Fig. 2.2.

Because the Gaussian distribution relates to a variable containing a large number of separate fluctuations combining to form the basic fluctuation, it has the widest of applications in the physical sciences. Many extensions are known, but reference to a textbook on statistics should be made for these.

2.6. THE LOG NORMAL DISTRIBUTION

This is related to the Gaussian distribution by the transformation

$$z = \ln x$$

and by eqn. (2.11):

$$p(x) = (1/2\pi x)\exp(-z^2/2)$$
$$= (1/2\pi x)\exp[-(\ln x)^2/2] \tag{2.14}$$

This distribution is sometimes used to describe surface pressure coefficients on buildings.

2.7. CHI-SQUARE DISTRIBUTION

When the windspeed V is composed of a number (n) of components, each of which follows a Gaussian distribution with zero mean and unit variance

$$x = z_1^2 + z_2^2 + z_3^2 \cdots + z_n^2 \tag{2.15}$$

the variable x follows a chi-square distribution whose probability density function is given by

$$p(x) = [2^{n/2}\Gamma(n/2)]^{-1}x^{[(n/2)-1]}\exp(-x/2) \tag{2.16}$$

where n is the number of degrees of freedom and $\Gamma(n/2)$ is the gamma function for $n/2$.

The mean value is

$$\bar{x} = n \tag{2.17}$$

and the variance

$$\sigma_x^2 = 2n \tag{2.18}$$

The probability density function and the cumulative distribution function are shown in Fig. 2.3 for a range of values of n.

Several special cases of the chi-square distribution are of interest. The windspeed V (not V^2 as in eqn. (2.16)) for the case of $n = 2$ follows a Rayleigh distribution

$$x = V^2, \qquad y = V$$

or

$$x = y^2, \qquad \mathrm{d}x/\mathrm{d}y = 2y$$

and from eqn. (2.11)

$$p(y) = (1/2y)\{[2\Gamma(1)]^{-1}\exp[-y^2/2]\}$$
$$= y\exp(-y^2/2) \tag{2.19}$$

This appears again in Section 2.11, when the mean and variance are derived.

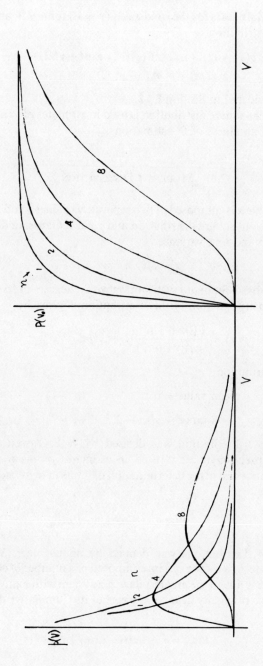

Fig. 2.3. Probability density function and cumulative distribution function for a chi-square distribution.

Another special case is for the windspeed ($y = V$) for $n = 3$, and is called the Maxwell distribution

$$p(y) = (1/2y)\{[2^{3/2}\Gamma(\tfrac{3}{2})]^{-1}y\exp(-y^2/2)\}$$
$$= (2/\pi)^{1/2}y^2\exp(-y^2/2) \qquad (2.20)$$

and this is considered in Section 2.12.

The general chi-square distribution is used in estimates of variance from samples and in goodness of fit estimations.

2.8.   STUDENT t DISTRIBUTION

When the variable x is composed of two separate variables y and z such that variable y has a chi-square distribution and z has a Gaussian distribution with zero mean and unit variance:

$$x = z/(y/n)^{1/2} \qquad (2.21)$$

then variable x has a Student t distribution with n degrees of freedom. The probability density function of this distribution is given by

$$p(x) = \frac{\Gamma[(n+1)/2]}{(\pi n)^{1/2}\Gamma(n/2)}[1 + x^2/n]^{-(n+1)/2} \qquad (2.22)$$

For this distribution,

$$\text{mean value} = 0 \qquad\qquad (n > 1) \qquad (2.23)$$

$$\text{variance} = n/(n - 2) \qquad (n > 2) \qquad (2.24)$$

The Student t distribution was devised by W. S. Gossett, who used Student as a pseudonym. It is used in estimates of mean value with estimated variance and in the determination of limits in regression analysis.

2.9.   WEIBULL DISTRIBUTION

This family of distributions was defined by an engineer, Weibull, to represent a model of a failure system composed of a number of components in which failure is due to the greatest flaw in a system with many flaws. The distribution was originally defined in terms of its Cumulative distribution function

$$P(x) = 1 - \exp[-(x/c)^k] \qquad (2.25)$$

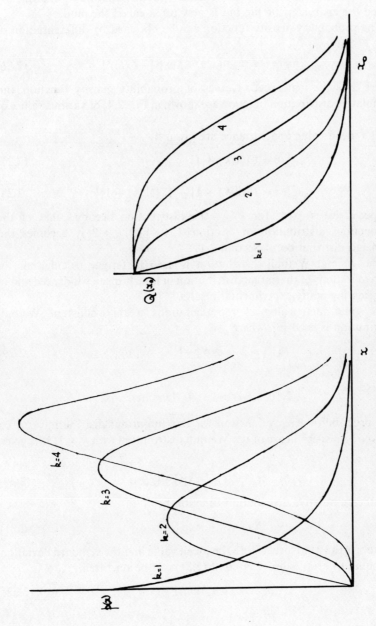

Fig. 2.4. Probability density function and cumulative distribution function for a Weibull distribution.

where x is the windspeed V, k is called the Weibull slope and c was originally called the characteristic life but is now often called the mode.

The probability density function can be obtained by differentiation of eqn. (2.25):

$$p(x) = (k/c)(x/c)^{k-1} \exp\left[-(x/c)^k\right] \qquad (2.26)$$

where x is the windspeed. Curves of probability density function and cumulative distribution function are shown in Fig. 2.4 for various values of k.

The mean value and variance are given by

$$\bar{x}/c = \Gamma[(1/k) + 1] \qquad (2.27)$$

and

$$\sigma_x^2/c^2 = \Gamma[(2/k) + 1] - \{\Gamma[(1/k) + 1]\}^2 \qquad (2.28)$$

Special cases exist: for $k = 1$ the distribution becomes that of the exponential distribution of Section 2.10. For $k = 2$ it becomes the Rayleigh distribution of Section 2.11.

The general Weibull distribution is used in fatigue calculations, in representations of the parent distribution of hourly mean windspeed and in representing many experimental results.

In some meteorological representations a three-constant Weibull distribution is used [6], where

$$P(V) = 1 - \exp\left\{-[(V - V_0)/c]^k\right\} \qquad (2.29)$$

2.10. EXPONENTIAL DISTRIBUTION

The probability density function for this important distribution can be derived as a special case of the Weibull distribution with $k = 1$. It is given by

$$p(x) = (1/c) \exp\left[-(x/c)\right] \qquad (2.30)$$

and the cumulative distribution function by

$$P(x) = 1 - \exp\left[-(x/c)\right] \qquad (2.31)$$

where x is the windspeed. Both the mean value and the standard deviation are equal to c, so eqns. (2.30) and (2.31) can be rewritten

$$p(x) = (1/\sigma_x) \exp\left[-(x/\sigma_x)\right] \qquad (2.32)$$

and

$$P(x) = 1 - \exp\left[-(x/\sigma_x)\right] \qquad (2.33)$$

This distribution is often applied to values of pressure coefficient on buildings where the mean value is large and negative or to structured wakes.

2.11. RAYLEIGH DISTRIBUTION

This is a well known distribution whose probability density function can be derived as a special case of both the chi-square distribution for V and the Weibull distribution with $k = 2$. Its probability density function has already been derived from the chi-square distribution in eqn. (2.19), but can equally well be calculated from the Weibull distribution with $k = 2$. Thus

$$p(x) = (2/c)(x/c)\exp\left[-(x/c)^2\right]$$

for which the standard deviation is given by eqn. (2.28) to be

$$\sigma_x/c = \{\Gamma(2) - [\Gamma(\tfrac{3}{2})]^2\}^{1/2}$$
$$= (1 - \pi/4)^{1/2}$$

or

$$c = 2\sigma_x/(4 - \pi)^{1/2}$$

so that

$$p(x) = \frac{(4 - \pi)}{2\sigma_x}\left(\frac{x}{\sigma_x}\right)\exp\left[-\frac{(4 - \pi)}{4}\left(\frac{x}{\sigma_x}\right)^2\right] \tag{2.34}$$

and

$$P(x) = 1 - \exp\left[-(x/c)^2\right]$$
$$= 1 - \exp\left\{-[(4 - \pi)/4][x/\sigma_x]^2\right\} \tag{2.35}$$

The Rayleigh distribution is applied to the windspeed near the ground when only two degrees of freedom exist.

2.12. MAXWELL DISTRIBUTION

This is a special case of the chi-square distribution for V with $k = 3$. The probability density function is given by eqn. (2.20):

$$p(x) = (2/\pi)^{1/2}x^2\exp\left[-x^2/2\right] \tag{2.36}$$

This has a mean value of $(8/\pi)^{1/2}$ and a standard deviation of $[(3\pi - 8)/\pi]^{1/2}$.

2.13. THE F DISTRIBUTION

Let x_1 and x_2 be independent random variables such that x_1 has a χ^2 distribution with n_1 degrees of freedom and x_2 has a χ^2 distribution with n_2 degrees of freedom. A new variable y can be defined as

$$y = (x_1/n_1)/(x_2/n_2) \tag{2.37}$$

and y is said to have an F distribution. This has a probability density function given by

$$p(y) = \frac{\Gamma[(n_1 + n_2)/2](n_1/n_2)^{n_1/2}y^{(n_1/2)-1}}{\Gamma(n_1/2)\Gamma(n_2/2)(1 + n_1 y/n_2)^{(n_1+n_2)/2}} \tag{2.38}$$

The mean and variance of the F distribution are given by

$$\bar{y} = n_2/(n_2 - 2) \qquad\qquad (n_2 > 2)$$

$$\sigma_y^2 = [2n_2^2(n_1 + n_2 - 2)]/[n_1(n_2 - 2)(n_2 - 4)] \qquad (n_2 > 4)$$

This distribution is applied to the ratio of variances in the hypothesis test described in Section 6.3.

2.14. BINOMIAL DISTRIBUTION

All former distributions have referred to random *continuous* variables: the binomial distribution refers to a discrete number of events and as such is of a quite different type. There are many more distributions of this type; this is the only one considered in these volumes. For other distributions the reader is referred to a book on statistics.

This probability distribution is most easily explained by an example. Suppose a dice is thrown 10 times. At each throw, which constitutes a trial, assuming the dice is unbiased the probability of throwing a 6 is $\frac{1}{6}$ and the probability of not throwing a 6 is $\frac{5}{6}$. Thus the probability of throwing no 6s in the 10 throws is $(\frac{5}{6})^{10}$.

Consider next the probability of throwing one 6 in the 10 throws. The probability that the first throw will be a 6 is $\frac{1}{6}$ and that the succeeding 9 throws will not be 6s is $(\frac{5}{6})^9$. But the 6 could be in any throw, so the probability of throwing one 6 is

$$_{10}C_1(\tfrac{1}{6})(\tfrac{5}{6})^9 = 10(\tfrac{1}{6})(\tfrac{5}{6})^9$$

The same argument for two 6s will give

$$_{10}C_2(\tfrac{1}{6})^2(\tfrac{5}{6})^8 = 45(\tfrac{1}{6})^2(\tfrac{5}{6})^8$$

and it becomes obvious that the probability of throwing n 6s is the $(n + 1)^{\text{th}}$ term in the series

$$[\tfrac{1}{6} + \tfrac{5}{6}]^{10}$$

which is

$$_{10}C_n(\tfrac{1}{6})^n(\tfrac{5}{6})^{(10-n)}$$

In general, if Q_1 is the probability that an event will happen in one trial and P_1 is the probability that an event will not happen in one trial, then

$$(P_1 + Q_1) = 1$$

The probability that an event will occur r times in N trials will be

$$_NC_rP_1^{N-r}Q_1^r$$

or, more specifically, the probability that an event will not happen in N trials is equal to P_1^N. Thus

$$P_N = P_1^N \tag{2.39}$$

2.15. JOINT PROBABILITY

So far the discussion has centred around the probability that a single variable shall have a given value. There are many instances when it is required to know the probability that two variables x and y shall each have a stated value simultaneously. This can be shown as a data acquisition problem akin to the definition of probability density function in Fig. 1.5.

In Fig. 2.5 the variation with time of two variables x and y is shown. Lines representing instances at which readings of x and y were taken and cells for the x and y variables could be superimposed on this figure in the same way that they were superimposed on Fig. 1.5 for the single variable. Suppose a particular value (cell) of x is chosen and the numbers of readings in all the cells of the y variable when that value of x occurs are recorded. It would then be possible to draw a probability density function for y for that value of x. When the process is repeated for a range of values of x, a whole series of probability density functions for y are obtained. When these are all combined onto a single picture as in Fig. 2.6, it becomes obvious that the result is a three-dimensional shape when the cell sizes are reduced to zero. The cumulative distribution function

$$\text{Prob}\,[x_1 < x < x_2, y_1 < y < y_2] = \int_{y_1}^{y_2} \int_{x_1}^{x_2} p(x, y)\,\mathrm{d}x\,\mathrm{d}y \tag{2.40}$$

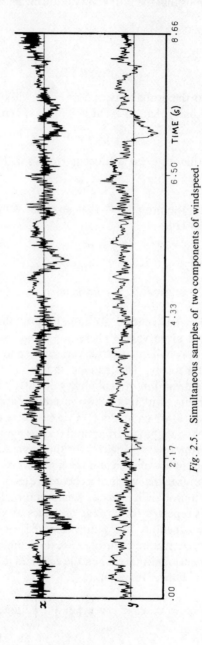

Fig. 2.5. Simultaneous samples of two components of windspeed.

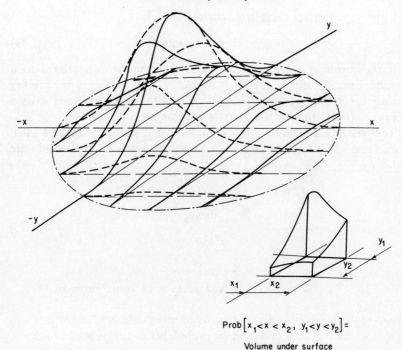

Prob$\left[x_1 < x < x_2, \; y_1 < y < y_2\right] =$

Volume under surface

Fig. 2.6. Joint probability distribution.

is equal to the volume under the curve which projects the area bounded by $x_1 \, x_2 \, y_1$ and y_2 on the plane $p(x, y) = 0$. It follows immediately that

$$\text{Prob}\left[-\infty < x < \infty, \, -\infty < y < \infty\right] = \int_{-\infty}^{\infty} \int_{-\infty}^{\infty} p(x,y) \, \mathrm{d}x \, \mathrm{d}y = 1 \tag{2.41}$$

It also follows from the above definition that

$$p(x) = \int_{-\infty}^{\infty} p(x,y) \, \mathrm{d}y \tag{2.42a}$$

and

$$p(y) = \int_{-\infty}^{\infty} p(x,y) \, \mathrm{d}x \tag{2.42b}$$

If the variables are statistically independent

$$p(x,y) = p(x)p(y) \tag{2.43}$$

If the variables are completely correlated

$$p(x, y) = p(x) = p(y) \tag{2.44}$$

If the variables are partly correlated the expression is related to a covariance coefficient $c_{xy}(0)$ given by eqn. (1.23). The joint probability density function is a function of x, y and $c_{xy}(0)$ and is sometimes written $p(x_1 y_1 c_{xy}(0))$, although this form is uncommon.

The general expression for this is cumbersome, so the special case when both x and y have Gaussian distributions will be quoted here. If x and y are redefined as

$$z_1 = (x - \bar{x})/\sigma_x \qquad z_2 = (y - \bar{y})/\sigma_y$$

$$p(z_1, z_2) = \frac{\exp\{[z_1^2 - 2c_{z_1 z_2}(0)z_1 z_2 + z_2^2]/[-2(1 - c_{z_1 z_2}^2(0))]\}}{2\pi[1 - c_{z_1 z_2}^2(0)]^{1/2}} \tag{2.45}$$

2.16. TRANSFORMATION OF VARIABLES WITH JOINT PROBABILITY

When two variables r and s are both known but different functions of two more variables x and y, and the joint probability density function for x and y is known, it is possible to determine the joint probability of the variables r and s.

If

$$r = f_1(x, y) \qquad \text{and} \qquad s = f_2(x, y)$$

it is possible to solve these equations for x and y to obtain

$$x = \phi_1(r, s) \qquad y = \phi_2(r, s)$$

The required joint probability density function $p(r, s)$ is then equal to

$$p(r, s) = p(x, y)|J(r, s)| \tag{2.46}$$

where $J(r, s)$ is called the Jacobian of the transformation $(x, y) \rightarrow (r, s)$ and is given by

$$J(r, s) = \begin{vmatrix} \partial x/\partial r & \partial x/\partial s \\ \partial y/\partial r & \partial y/\partial s \end{vmatrix} \tag{2.47}$$

It is obvious that this resolves itself into eqn. (2.11) for the single-variable case. The same procedure can be extended to as many variables as required.

2.17. JOINT PROBABILITY OF RELATED QUANTITIES

Consider as an example the pressure P at a location. It is related to the local pressure coefficient C_p and the windspeed $\bar{U}$ by the equation

$$P = \tfrac{1}{2} C_p \rho \bar{U}^2 \tag{2.48}$$

If the windspeed is the hourly average windspeed $\bar{U}$ (low-pass cut-off at a period of one hour) and the pressure coefficient is related only to the micrometeorological part of the spectrum (high-pass cut-off at a period of one hour), C_p and $\bar{U}$ are statistically independent, so eqn. (2.43) applies. Thus

$$p(C_p, \bar{U}) = p(C_p)p(\bar{U}) \tag{2.49}$$

Since the pressure is a simple function of C_p and $\bar{U}$, the joint probability of P and $\bar{U}$ can be calculated using the procedures of the last paragraph:

$$r = P \qquad x = C_p$$
$$s = \bar{U} \qquad y = \bar{U}$$

$$p(P, \bar{U}) = p(C_p, \bar{U}) \begin{vmatrix} \partial C_p / \partial P & \partial C_p / \partial \bar{U} \\ \partial \bar{U} / \partial P & \partial \bar{U} / \partial \bar{U} \end{vmatrix}$$

$$= p(C_p, \bar{U}) \partial C_p / \partial P \tag{2.50}$$

because $\partial C_p / \partial \bar{U} = 0$ as C_p and $\bar{U}$ are independent.

Similarly, it can be shown that

$$p(P, C_p) = p(C_p, \bar{U}) \partial \bar{U} / \partial P \tag{2.51}$$

so

$$p(P) = \int_0^\infty p(P, \bar{U}) \, \mathrm{d}\bar{U} = \int_{-\infty}^\infty p(P, C_p) \, \mathrm{d}C_p \tag{2.52}$$

It follows from eqn. (2.8) that the cumulative distribution function is given by

$$Q(P_0) = \int_{P_0}^\infty p(P) \, \mathrm{d}P$$

$$= \int_{P_0}^\infty \int_0^\infty p(P, \bar{U}) \, \mathrm{d}\bar{U} \, \mathrm{d}P = \int_{P_0}^\infty \int_{-\infty}^\infty p(P, C_p) \, \mathrm{d}C_p \, \mathrm{d}P$$

$$\tag{2.53}$$

There are moves at present to determine extreme values of windspeed as functions of wind direction also. The above analysis applies to that situation as well. Equation (2.49) would become

$$p(C_p, \bar{U}, \theta) = p(C_p, \theta)p(\bar{U}, \theta) \tag{2.54}$$

$$r = P \qquad x = C_p$$
$$s = \bar{U} \qquad y = \bar{U}$$
$$t = \theta \qquad z = \theta$$

$$p(P, \bar{U}, \theta) = p(C_p, \bar{U}, \theta) \begin{vmatrix} \partial C_p/\partial P & \partial C_p/\partial \bar{U} & \partial C_p/\partial \theta \\ \partial \bar{U}/\partial P & \partial \bar{U}/\partial \bar{U} & \partial \bar{U}/\partial \theta \\ \partial \theta/\partial P & \partial \theta/\partial \bar{U} & \partial \theta/\partial \theta \end{vmatrix}$$

$$= p(C_p, \bar{U}, \theta) \, \partial C_p/\partial P \tag{2.55}$$

and by a similar process

$$p(P, C_p, \theta) = p(C_p, \bar{U}, \theta) \, \partial \bar{U}/\partial P \tag{2.56}$$

with the final cumulative distribution function

$$Q(P_0, \theta_1, \theta_2) = \int_{P_0}^{\infty} \int_{0}^{\infty} \int_{\theta_1}^{\theta_2} p(P, \bar{U}, \theta) \, d\theta \, d\bar{U} \, dP \tag{2.57}$$

3

Statistics: Autocovariance and Spectral Density Functions for a Single Variable at One Point in Space

In the broad-brush treatment in Chapter 1, it was stated that the autocovariance function partly defines the time domain and the spectral density function the frequency domain, and that they are related by a Fourier transformation. In this chapter the two functions are defined for a single variable and their relationship determined. In the next chapter the corresponding quantities for either two components at one location or one component at two locations are developed.

In the next two chapters the terms correlation and covariance will occur several times. The difference between the two is one of definition. In these volumes correlation will be applied to the whole windspeed (i.e. mean plus fluctuating part) whereas covariance only applies to the fluctuating part. Thus, as in eqn. (1.4),

$$V = \bar{U} + u(t) \tag{3.1}$$

The autocorrelation function is defined as

$$R_{VV}(\tau) = \overline{[\bar{U} + u(t)][\bar{U} + u(t + \tau)]} \tag{3.2}$$

and the autocovariance function as

$$C_{uu}(\tau) = \overline{u(t)u(t + \tau)} \tag{3.3}$$

It follows from eqns. (3.2) and (3.3) that

$$R_{VV}(\tau) = \bar{U}^2 + C_{uu}(\tau) \tag{3.4}$$

Throughout the volumes correlation, covariance and spectral density functions have always been given two subscripts. These define the two quantities composing the function. Thus in eqn. (3.3) $C_{uu}(\tau)$ means that it represents the covariance function for windspeed u with itself delayed by time interval τ. The term $C_{u_1 u_2}(\tau)$ would represent the covariance function

37

for the windspeed at location 1 with the windspeed at location 2 delayed by a time interval τ.

3.1. AUTOCORRELATION AND AUTOCOVARIANCE FUNCTIONS

These two functions are defined by eqns. (3.2) and (3.3). It is often convenient to work in non-dimensional form, so two coefficients are defined from the functions; they have the same symbol but are lower case characters.

$$\text{Autocorrelation coefficient: } r_{VV}(\tau) = R_{VV}(\tau)/\sigma_u^2 \tag{3.5}$$

$$\text{Autocovariance coefficient: } c_{uu}(\tau) = C_{uu}(\tau)/\sigma_u^2 \tag{3.6}$$

The autocovariance coefficient is a function of time. It would be convenient to define a single number to represent the whole curve; such a number is called the 'integral time scale'. This is defined in terms of the autocovariance coefficient by the relationship

$$T_u = \int_0^\infty c_{uu}(\tau) \, d\tau \tag{3.7}$$

A similar device is used to relate covariance for special intervals; these are called integral length scales and are defined in Section 4.9.

3.2. DEFINITION OF THE SPECTRAL DENSITY FUNCTION

The fluctuating component of windspeed can be written

$$u(t) = \int_0^\infty [I_1(n)\cos 2\pi nt + I_2(n)\sin 2\pi nt] \, dn \tag{3.8}$$

The variance of the windspeed is therefore

$$\sigma_u^2 = \frac{1}{T} \int_0^T u^2(t) \, dt$$

$$= \frac{1}{T} \int_0^T \int_0^\infty [I_1(n)\cos 2\pi nt + I_2(n)\sin 2\pi nt]^2 \, dn \, dt$$

$$= \frac{1}{T} \int_0^T \int_0^\infty \{[I_1^2(n) + I_2^2(n)]/2\} \, dn \, dt$$

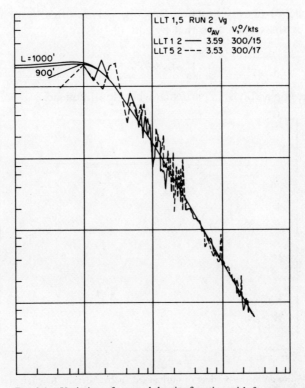

Fig. 3.1. Variation of spectral density function with frequency.

as all cross-terms $I_1(n_1)I_2(n_2)$, $I_1(n_1)I_1(n_2)$, $I_2(n_1)I_2(n_2)$, etc., integrate to zero.

The spectral density function $(S_{uu}(n))$ is defined as equal to the term

$$S_{uu}(n) = \frac{1}{T} \int_0^T \{[I_1^2(n) + I_2^2(n)]/2\}\, dt \tag{3.9}$$

so that

$$\sigma_u^2 = \int_0^\infty S_{uu}(n)\, dn \tag{3.10}$$

Sometimes this definition is put into different symbols

$$S_{uu}(n) = \lim_{\Delta n \to 0} [\sigma_u^2(n, \Delta n)/\Delta_n]$$

The spectral density function (see Fig. 3.1) is often 'normalised' by dividing by the variance, so that by eqn. (3.10)

$$\int_0^\infty S_{uu}(n)/\sigma_u^2 = 1 \tag{3.11}$$

In some applications, in particular where low frequencies are of interest,

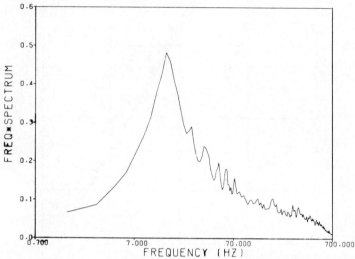

Fig. 3.2. Variation of the product of normalised spectral density function and frequency with frequency.

it is preferable to use a logarithmic scale for frequency. In that case it is usual to use the form (see Fig. 3.2)

$$\int_{-\infty}^\infty [nS_{uu}(n)/\sigma_u^2]\,d(\ln n) = 1 \tag{3.12}$$

or

$$\int_{-\infty}^\infty [nS_{uu}(n)/\sigma_u^2]\,d(\log n) = 2\cdot303 \tag{3.13}$$

$S_{uu}(n)$ is called a one-sided spectrum because the frequency range is from zero to infinity. A two-sided spectrum $G_{uu}(n)$ exists which has a frequency range from minus infinity to plus infinity. The concept of negative frequency is difficult to comprehend until it is converted into circular measure, when

$$2\pi n = \omega = \dot{\theta} \tag{3.14}$$

when negative frequency is seen to be merely a negative direction of rotation. The relationship between the one-sided and two-sided spectra is

$$S_{uu}(n) = 2G_{uu}(n) \qquad 0 < n < \infty \qquad (3.15)$$

3.3. RELATIONSHIP BETWEEN SPECTRAL DENSITY FUNCTION AND AUTOCOVARIANCE FUNCTION

An expression for the autocovariance can be calculated from the definition of windspeed in eqn. (3.8):

$$
\begin{aligned}
C_{uu}(\tau) &= \frac{1}{T} \int_0^T u(t)u(t + \tau)\,\mathrm{d}t \\
&= \frac{1}{T} \int_0^\infty \int_0^T \{I_1(n)\cos 2\pi nt + I_2(n)\sin 2\pi nt\} \\
&\quad \times \{I_1(n)\cos 2\pi n(t + \tau) + I_2(n)\sin 2\pi n(t + \tau)\}\,\mathrm{d}t\,\mathrm{d}n \\
&= \frac{1}{T} \int_0^\infty \int_0^T \tfrac{1}{2}[I_1^2(n) + I_2^2(n)]\cos 2\pi n\tau \,\mathrm{d}t\,\mathrm{d}n
\end{aligned}
$$

which, by eqn. (3.9), is equal to

$$C_{uu}(\tau) = \int_0^\infty S_{uu}(n)\cos 2\pi n\tau \,\mathrm{d}n \qquad (3.16)$$

This is the conventional Fourier transformation. It therefore follows by Parseval's theorem that the inverse relationship applies:

$$S_{uu}(n) = 4 \int_0^\infty C_{uu}(\tau)\cos 2\pi n\tau \,\mathrm{d}\tau \qquad (3.17)$$

Note that the number 4 occurs because $S_{uu}(n)$ is a one-sided spectral density function.

3.4. EVALUATION OF SPECTRAL DENSITY FUNCTION FROM THE AUTOCOVARIANCE FUNCTION

When an analytical function for the autocovariance is known, the spectral density function can be evaluated from eqn. (3.17). For example, if the autocovariance function is exponential

$$C_{uu}(\tau) = \exp(-k\tau)$$

then

$$S_{uu}(n) = 4 \int_0^\infty \exp(-k\tau) \cos 2\pi n\tau \, d\tau$$

$$= 4k/(k^2 + 4\pi^2 n^2)$$

To derive the spectral density function from experimental data using a digital computer, it is easy to calculate the autocovariance function by multiplication and averaging and then to calculate the spectral density function by means of the Fourier transformation (eqn. (3.17)). This is the original procedure; it is called the Blackman–Tukey method, but is rarely used now because it is slow. The method is given in detail on page 315 *et seq.* of Bendat and Piersol [3].

3.5. Spectral Density Function by Fast Fourier Transform

In the previous paragraph the spectral density function was evaluated by the Fourier transformation of the autocovariance function (see eqn. (3.17)). To perform this operation the autocovariance function must first be evaluated from the raw data and stored, and then the Fourier transformation performed on the stored data. This is a slow process.

The spectral density function can be derived directly from the raw data. This can clearly be seen from eqns. (3.8) and (3.9). In a digital application the integral form of eqn. (3.8) must be replaced by the summation

$$u(q) = \sum_{n=1}^{N/2} I_1(n) \cos(2\pi qn/N) + \sum_{n=1}^{(N/2)-1} I_2(n) \sin(2\pi qn/N) \quad (3.18)$$

and the values of I are given by

$$\left. \begin{array}{c} I_1(n) = (2/N) \displaystyle\sum_{q=1}^{N} u(q) \cos(2\pi qn/N) \\[2em] I_1(N/2) = (1/N) \displaystyle\sum_{q=1}^{N} u(q) \cos q\pi \end{array} \right\} \quad (3.19)$$

and

$$I_2(n) = (1/N) \sum_{q=1}^{N} u(q) \sin(2\pi qn/N)$$

For the digital computer to solve these equations it would require 2^N multiply-and-add operations. The fast Fourier transform technique breaks down the process into a number of elements so that the final result is a product of these elements, some of which, having been calculated once, can be used many times. A special case of the FFT, called the Cooley–Tukey method, in which the number of readings must be a power of 2, is the quickest in operation and consequently the most popular. The details of the computation are available in many textbooks (for example, on pages 302 *et seq.* of Bendat and Piersol [3]).

3.6. SPECTRAL DENSITY FUNCTION BY FILTERING

The analogue method to obtain a spectral density function is to filter the windspeed, square and average. When the windspeed of eqn. (3.8) is filtered to leave only frequency n, it becomes

$$u(t, n) = [I_1(n)\cos 2\pi nt + I_2(n)\sin 2\pi nt]\,\Delta n$$

and by eqn. (3.9)

$$S_{uu}(n)\,\Delta n = \frac{1}{T}\int_0^T \{[I_1^2(n) + I_2^2(n)]/2\}\,dt = \sigma_u^2(n, \Delta n)$$

or

$$S_{uu}(n) = \sigma_u^2(n, \Delta n)/\Delta n$$

In Jones's statistical discrete gust work (Section 3.7), the quantity $[u(t) - u(t + \tau)]$ is used to present data in a form suitable for the design of aircraft in turbulence. Either by using eqn. (3.8) or by using the expressions for the variance and autocovariance functions, it can be shown that the variance of this quantity is related to the spectral density function:

$$\overline{[u(t) - u(t + \tau)]^2} = \overline{u^2(t)} + \overline{u^2(t + \tau)} - \overline{2u(t)u(t + \tau)}$$

$$= 2[\overline{u^2(t)} - C_{uu}(\tau)]$$

$$= 2\left[\int_0^\infty S_{uu}(n)\,dn - \int_0^\infty S_{uu}(n)\cos 2\pi n\tau\,dn\right]$$

$$= 2\int_0^\infty S_{uu}(n)[1 - \cos 2\pi n\tau]\,dn$$

3.7. STATISTICAL DISCRETE GUST METHOD

In the early days of aviation, the response of an aircraft to turbulence was estimated by exposing a mathematic model of the aircraft to a mathematically defined discrete gust. In the 1950s the spectral approach was introduced and rapidly gained acceptance. But the spectral methods gave answers at times which were obviously wildly at odds with the old discrete gust method and modifications without number were proposed, each with its own drawback. About 1968 Glyn Jones at the Royal Aircraft Establishment proposed a new method which was a link between the spectral and the old discrete gust method, and he called it the 'statistical discrete gust'. Over the last decade this method [26] has been developed further and controversy still reigns. An extension of the method is presented here because the author is convinced that it will become a powerful tool in several fields, including building aerodynamics. Although developed for wind turbulence, its applicability is much wider and it can be applied to the measurement of pressures or any other measurement. Whilst the method presented here is due to the author, it is only an extension of the original work by Glyn Jones to whom all credit for its inception is due. There follows an outline of the method.

For the sake of this outline the property studied will be called 'windspeed'. The steps of the method are:

(i)   Collect a sample of windspeed V and digitise at a constant reading rate RR. Compute the mean value of windspeed $\bar{U}$ and the standard deviation σ_d.

(ii)   A lag S is chosen and the original data are converted into a new variable U with S less data points by the relationship

$$U_i = u_i - u_{i+s} \qquad (3.20)$$

where u_i and u_{i+s} are the ith and the $(i + S)$th reading and the units of S are the numbers of readings.

(iii) For the chosen value of lag S, a time lag τ between the readings can be calculated as

$$\tau = S/RR \qquad (3.21)$$

and the mean value $\bar{U}$ and standard deviation σ_τ are determined. In every instance so far studied, $\bar{U} = 0$.

(iv)   A frequency n can be defined as

$$n = 1/2\tau = RR/2S \qquad (3.22)$$

By definition

$$\sigma_\tau^2 = \frac{1}{N-S-1} \sum_{i=1}^{N-S} (u_i - u_{i+s})^2$$

$$= \frac{1}{N-S-1} \sum_{i=1}^{N-S} u_i^2 - 2 \sum_{i=1}^{N-S} u_i u_{i+s} + \sum_{i=1}^{N-S} u_{i+s}^2$$

$$= 2\sigma_d^2 - 2C_{uu}(\tau)$$

$$= 2\sigma_d^2 \left\{ 1 - \int_0^\infty [S_{uu}(n)/\sigma_d^2] \cos 2\pi n\tau \, dn \right\} \quad \text{by eqn. (3.16)}$$

or

$$\sigma_\tau^2/\sigma_d^2 = 2 \int_0^\infty [nS_{uu}(n)/\sigma_d^2](1 - \cos 2\pi n\tau) \, d(\ln n) \tag{3.23}$$

(v) A new value of lag is chosen and steps (i) to (iv) are repeated. At Bristol the lags form a binary series (4, 8, 16, 32, etc., to 512).

(vi) A specific normalised spectrum $nS_{uu}(n)/\sigma_d^2$ is a function of (n/n_p) only, where n_p is the frequency of the peak of the $nS_{uu}(n)/\sigma_d^2 \sim \ln n$ curve. Equation (3.23) shows that a family of normalised spectra can be written

$$nS_{uu}(n)/\sigma_d^2 = f[(n/n_p), \sigma_{\tau_p}/\sigma_d] \tag{3.24}$$

where τ_p is the time lag related to the frequency n_p by eqn. (3.22).

In a specific spectrum it is possible to write for an individual frequency n_i

$$n_i S_{uu}(n_i) = \sigma_{\tau_i}^2/R \tag{3.25}$$

where n_i and τ_i are related by eqns. (3.21) and (3.22), and so for this spectrum

$$R = f(n/n_p)$$

and for the family of spectra

$$R = f[(n/n_p), \sigma_{\tau_p}/\sigma_d] \tag{3.26}$$

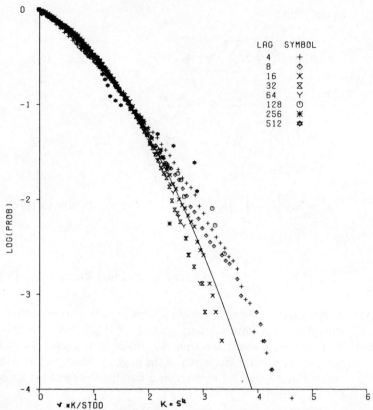

Fig. 3.3.   Statistical discrete gust method—cumulative distribution function for a variable
with a Gaussian distribution.

(vii)   The cumulative distribution function (CDF) for the new variable is
defined as

$$Q(\bar{U}_0) = \int_{\bar{U}_0}^{\infty} p(\bar{U})\, \mathrm{d}\bar{U}$$

and can be plotted separately for each lag. It is current practice in
statistics to divide a variable by its standard deviation to obtain a
new non-dimensional variable which has a more general application. Thus

$$Q(\bar{U}_0/\sigma_\tau) = \int_{\bar{U}_0/\sigma_\tau}^{\infty} p(\bar{U}/\sigma_\tau)\, \mathrm{d}(\bar{U}/\sigma_\tau) \tag{3.27}$$

can be presented for experimental data. Also superimposed on any set of experimental results can be any known distribution from Chapter 2 of this volume.

(viii) Define a new parameter K such that

$$K = \sigma_{\mathrm{d}}/\sigma_{\tau} \tag{3.28}$$

and it immediately follows from eqns. (3.23) and (3.24) that

$$K = f[(n/n_{\mathrm{p}}), \sigma_{\tau_{\mathrm{p}}}/\sigma_{\mathrm{d}}] \tag{3.29}$$

Equation (3.27) for the CDF can be rewritten

$$Q(U_0 K/\sigma_{\mathrm{d}}) = \int_{U_0 K/\sigma_{\mathrm{d}}}^{\infty} p(UK/\sigma_{\mathrm{d}})\, \mathrm{d}(UK/\sigma_{\mathrm{d}})$$

and this expression is common for all lags as well as for the known distributions of Chapter 2, so all can be plotted on a common curve. Figure 3.3 shows such a presentation, on which has been superimposed the curve for the Gaussian distribution.

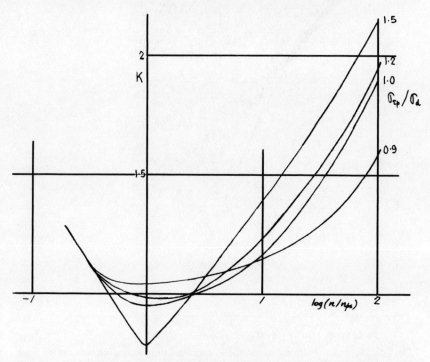

Fig. 3.4. Statistical discrete gust method—variation of parameter K with frequency ratio and standard deviation ratio.

(ix) The implication of this form of presentation is that as σ_d is a unique value for the sample, should the curves for all the lags collapse into a single curve as is the case in Fig. 3.3, then the occurrence of all values of UK within the sample are equally probable. The function for eqn. (3.29) derived experimentally is presented in Fig. 3.4 and from this it is noted that K is a minimum at $n = n_p$. At that frequency, the windspeed difference $\bar{U}$ which has the probability Q associated with the product UK will be a maximum. Thus Fig. 3.4 evaluates the probability of exceedence of a constituent of the sample of magnitude U and frequency n.

For a given lag (and therefore frequency), should the data not follow the Gaussian curve (as in Fig. 3.5) then, for the given

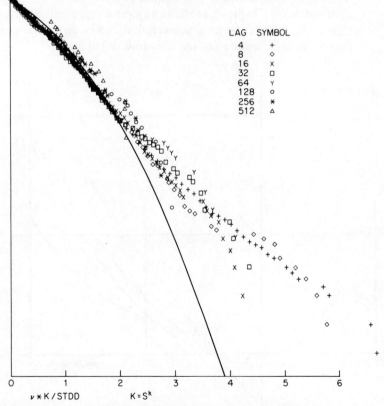

LAG	SYMBOL
4	+
8	◇
16	x
32	□
64	Y
128	o
256	*
512	△

$\nu * K / STDD$ $K = S^k$

Fig. 3.5. Statistical discrete gust method—cumulative distribution function for the cross-wind component of windspeed in clear air turbulence.

probability of exceedence, higher values (if above the Gaussian curve) of UK will occur. As K is independent of the shape of the distribution curve, this means that higher values of U will occur with that probability of exceedence. There are therefore two unrelated reasons for high values of windspeed having the same probability of exceedence; their frequency relative to the frequency at the peak of the spectrum and the shape of the CDF.

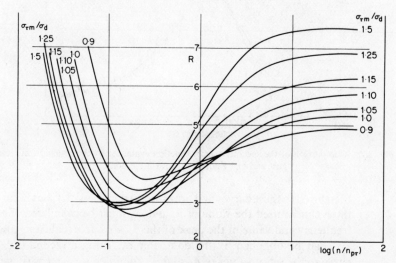

Fig. 3.6. Statistical discrete gust method—variation of parameter R with frequency ratio and standard deviation ratio.

(x) If it is possible to evolve experimentally the function for K in eqn. (3.29), it is equally possible to evaluate the function R in eqn. (3.26). This has been done and the results are presented in Fig. 3.6. Once this relationship is known it is possible to use this procedure to produce spectra by using eqns. (3.25). Because the lags chosen at Bristol form a binary series, octave spectra are produced. Figure 3.7 shows spectra, for the sample whose results are presented in Fig. 3.3, derived by this method as well as by the FFT technique of Section 3.5.

(xi) There are some practical difficulties which have to be overcome. To produce the equivalent of Fig. 3.3 within the computer, the functional relationship for K (eqn. (3.29)) presented in Fig. 3.4 must be converted into equation form. Fourth-order polynomials have

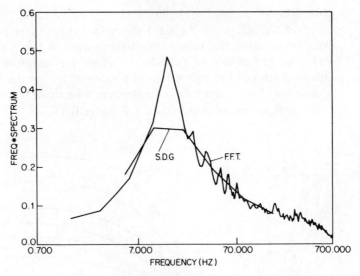

FREQUENCY (HZ)

Fig. 3.7. Comparison of the spectral density function evaluated by the statistical discrete gust and fast Fourier transform methods.

been fitted to these curves and are presented in Table 3.1, but before these can be used the value of n_p and σ_{τ_p} must be calculated. The frequency and value of the peak of the $\sigma_\tau \sim n$ curve (called n_{p_τ} and σ_{τ_m}) can be obtained by the computer by fitting a second-order curve to the set of values of n_{p_τ} and σ_{τ_m} obtained from steps (i) and (ii); but these values are not equal to the required values n_p and σ_{τ_p} unless $dR/d[\log (n/n_p)]$ is zero at the peak frequency. A glance at Fig. 3.6 will show that this is not the case, but the same glance will show that it is reasonable to assume that $dR/d[\log (n/n_p)]$ has a constant value between the two peak values. The values of R and $dR/d[\log (n/n_p)]$ in this region are given the suffix 0, and the values derived are

$$R_0 = 162\cdot3 - 508\cdot6Y + 599\cdot3Y^2 - 307\cdot2Y^3 + 58\cdot1Y^4 \quad (3.30)$$

and

$$|dR/d[\log (n/n_{p_\tau})]|_0$$
$$= 139\cdot8 - 495\cdot4Y + 641\cdot3Y^2 - 357\cdot6Y^3 + 73\cdot3Y^4 \quad (3.31)$$

where $Y = \sigma_{\tau_m}/\sigma_d$.

An iterative method is used to derive values of n_{p_τ} and the

Table 3.1. *Statistical gust method—table of equations showing the variation of parameter K with frequency and standard deviation ratios*

n/n_p	σ_{r_p}/σ_d	K	$\times 1$	$\times \log(n/n_p)$	$\times \log^2(n/n_p)$	$\times \log^3(n/n_p)$	$\times \log^4(n/n_p)$
$<1{\cdot}0$	$\sigma_{r_p}/\sigma_d < 0{\cdot}95$		$0{\cdot}021\,103$	$+0{\cdot}155\,799$	$+0{\cdot}893\,577$	$+0{\cdot}830\,771$	$+0{\cdot}355\,092$
	$0{\cdot}95 \le \sigma_{r_p}/\sigma_d < 1{\cdot}05$		$+0$	$+0{\cdot}094\,553$	$+0{\cdot}622\,530$	$+0{\cdot}222\,127$	$+0{\cdot}088\,051$
	$1{\cdot}05 \le \sigma_{r_p}/\sigma_d < 1{\cdot}25$		$-0{\cdot}024\,526$	$-0{\cdot}059\,556$	$+0{\cdot}432\,185$	$+0{\cdot}189\,184$	$+0{\cdot}114\,858$
	$\sigma_{r_p}/\sigma_d \ge 1{\cdot}25$		$-0{\cdot}106\,410$	$-0{\cdot}164\,575$	$+0{\cdot}908\,986$	$+1{\cdot}250\,548$	$+0{\cdot}571\,130$
$\ge 1{\cdot}0$	$\sigma_{r_p}/\sigma_d < 0{\cdot}95$		$+0{\cdot}021\,103$	$-0{\cdot}014\,243$	$+0{\cdot}039\,693$	$-0{\cdot}021\,829$	$+0{\cdot}005\,645$
	$0{\cdot}95 \le \sigma_{r_p}/\sigma_d < 1{\cdot}05$		$+0$	$-0{\cdot}019\,326$	$+0{\cdot}088\,578$	$-0{\cdot}037\,685$	$+0{\cdot}005\,099$
	$1{\cdot}05 \le \sigma_{r_p}/\sigma_d < 1{\cdot}25$		$-0{\cdot}024\,526$	$+0{\cdot}045\,862$	$+0{\cdot}068\,051$	$-0{\cdot}055\,798$	$+0{\cdot}012\,748$
	$\sigma_{r_p}/\sigma_d \ge 1{\cdot}25$		$-0{\cdot}106\,410$	$+0{\cdot}358\,754$	$-0{\cdot}259\,135$	$+0{\cdot}092\,609$	$-0{\cdot}012\,748$

Table 3.2. *Statistical gust method—Table of equations showing the variation of parameter R with frequency and standard deviation ratios*

$\log(n/n_p)$	σ_{τ_p}/σ_d	$R=$	$\times 1$	$\times \log(n/n_p)$	$\times \log^2(n/n_p)$	$\times \log^3(n/n_p)$	$\times \log^4(n/n_p)$
	$\sigma_{\tau_p}/\sigma_d < 0.90$		52.5784	+239.7766	+431.8447	+341.5404	+101.8939
	$0.90 \leq \sigma_{\tau_p}/\sigma_d < 1.0$		1.9359	-10.3060	-23.3390	-19.4474	-4.4143
< -0.6	$1.0 \leq \sigma_{\tau_p}/\sigma_d < 1.1$		2.2820	-3.3781	-8.2978	-6.8182	-1.1072
	$1.1 \leq \sigma_{\tau_p}/\sigma_d < 1.15$		3.3869	-1.7994	-7.5074	-6.1802	-0.9105
	$1.15 \leq \sigma_{\tau_p}/\sigma_d < 1.25$		4.1715	+1.0130	-2.7844	-2.6076	-0.0255
	$\sigma_{\tau_p}/\sigma_d \geq 1.25$		4.2766	+2.5993	+2.2948	+2.3681	+1.4205
	$\sigma_{\tau_p}/\sigma_d < 0.95$		4.0459	+0.8572	+0.0079	-0.2230	+0.0566
	$0.95 \leq \sigma_{\tau_p}/\sigma_d < 1.03$		3.9368	+1.3681	+0.2472	-0.6496	+0.1727
≥ -0.6	$1.03 \leq \sigma_{\tau_p}/\sigma_d < 1.08$		3.8302	+1.8217	+0.2142	-0.8239	+0.2314
	$1.08 \leq \sigma_{\tau_p}/\sigma_d < 1.13$		3.9926	+2.3126	-0.3264	-0.5831	+0.1967
	$1.13 \leq \sigma_{\tau_p}/\sigma_d < 1.20$		4.4278	+2.4345	-0.4806	-0.5885	+0.2227
	$1.20 \leq \sigma_{\tau_p}/\sigma_d < 1.35$		4.7926	+3.0473	-0.4355	-1.0280	+0.3712
	$\sigma_{\tau_p}/\sigma_d \geq 1.35$		5.1307	+3.7429	-0.3662	-1.5844	+0.5684

corresponding value σ_{τ_p}. The expressions for the factor K are based upon n_p and σ_{τ_p}.

For the computer to present spectra directly, the curves of Fig. 3.6 have been fitted by fourth-order polynomials and the expressions are given in Table 3.2.

This method has not been used in building aerodynamics as yet: it is included here because the author is convinced that, when it is better known and more widely used, it will prove a very valuable method.

The concept and development of the method are due to Glyn Jones, who was concerned with aircraft response to turbulence. In his studies only that part of the spectrum represented by

$$S_{uu}(n) \propto n^{-5/3}$$

was of interest, and in consequence Jones derived the simpler expression

$$K = S^{-1/3}$$

This can be shown to be the asymptotic value achieved by the expressions given in this paragraph.

3.8. MOMENTS OF THE SPECTRAL DENSITY FUNCTION

The basic spectral density function is defined as

$$\int_0^\infty S_{uu}(n)\,\mathrm{d}n = \sigma_u^2$$

Moments of the spectral density function are sometimes used. If

$$\psi_i = \int_0^\infty n^i S_{uu}(n)\,\mathrm{d}n = \int_{-\infty}^\infty n^{i+1} S_{uu}(n)\,\mathrm{d}(\ln n) \tag{3.32}$$

then ψ_i is called the ith moment of the spectral density function.

In practice, difficulty is encountered in the upper (∞) limit of the integration and this is often terminated at a finite value. Different values of ψ will be obtained for different upper limits and the value used in every evaluation ought to be studied with care. For example, in the evaluation of the spectral density function for a windspeed averaged over t seconds, the upper limit is often expressed as $1/t$ in the first form of eqn. (3.32).

One important application of these moments occurs in the study of independent events. When a sample of a time-varying parameter such as windspeed is measured, the upper frequency achievable is a function of the reading rate only, and if this is fast enough many readings will be taken within each 'event'.

Consider a specific parameter—the hourly average windspeed. The spectral density function would be derived from hourly average readings measured once an hour and the upper frequency limit would be $1/3600$ Hz. But windspeeds are generated by weather systems which have a variety of different times of passage, depending upon the size of the particular weather system, from a few minutes for the passage of a front to some four days for a large system. For the latter case, high windspeeds would be recorded hour after hour, but these high windspeeds would be 'related' to the single weather 'event'. Most statistical techniques apply to unrelated events and this batch of high values would upset the statistical implications. In consequence, the number of 'average unrelated events' should be used in place of the number of readings to obtain statistical information about frequency of occurrence and around these unrelated events a cluster of a number of hours of high (or low) windspeed can be assumed to occur. The average duration of an unrelated event is given as

$$T = (\psi_0/\psi_2)^{1/2} \qquad\qquad (3.33)$$

in the same units used for n in eqn. (3.32).

3.9. ALIASING

When digital methods are used to derive the spectral density function, care must be taken to avoid aliasing. This term implies that the contribution to the spectral density function from all frequencies above one-half of the digitisation rate will be credited to the wrong frequency.

In Fig. 3.8 a sample of a single frequency is shown in the full line. When digitised at a rate greater than twice its frequency the data will allow the correct frequency to be determined. When digitised at a rate less than twice the frequency (the square dots) the data will suggest a lower frequency. In practice the contribution to the spectral density function will be folded back and forth between the frequency limits of 0 and $f/2$, where f is the digitisation rate. This is shown in Fig. 3.9.

To prevent this a sample must always be *analogue* filtered before digitisation, at a frequency less than half the digitisation rate. Because an analogue filter does not have an instantaneous cut-off, in critical circumstances the filter ought to be set at between one-third and one-quarter of the digitisation rate. When correlations are being performed with

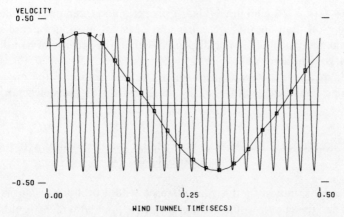

VELOCITY
0.50 —

-0.50 —

0.00   0.25   0.50

HIND TUNNEL TIME(SECS)

Fig. 3.8. Sample of the variation of windspeed with time to show aliasing.

filtered samples it must be remembered that most analogue filters introduce a phase shift at frequencies near cut-off. For accuracy with correlations it is advisable to digitise at a sufficiently high frequency, so that all the data required are at frequencies below about one-eighth of the digitisation rate.

A much faster digitisation rate with appropriate averaging of digital

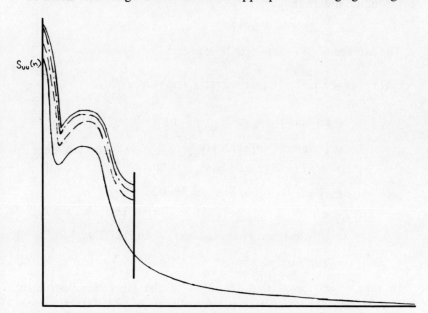

$S_{uu}(n)$

n

Fig. 3.9. Spectral density function showing fold-back of frequencies.

samples acts as a digital filter. This, if properly done, can produce a more
rapid cut-off than an analogue filter and does not introduce phase shift.
Thus an analogue filter can be dispensed with at the expense of handling a
very large volume of data.

Both methods in combination offer the best solution, the analogue
excluding unwanted high-frequency noise and the digital sharpening the
cut-off.

3.10. Effect of the Averaging Time of the Instrumentation and the Sample Length

In an ideal situation the instruments used would produce instantaneous
values and the sample would contain the whole population, i.e. would be of
infinite length. In practice, due to inertia of the measuring instrument, the
readings are averages over a given time (for example, a cup anemometer
gives a windspeed averaged over about $1 \cdot 5$ m of wind) and the sample length
is finite for economic reasons.

Consider the sample shown in Fig. 3.10. The fluctuating component of
the windspeed is given by eqn. (3.8). For simplicity, consider the
contribution due to frequency n:

$$u(t, n) = I_1(n) \cos 2\pi n t + I_2(n) \sin 2\pi n t$$

The average of this value over time interval s is given by

$$u(t_1, n, s) = \frac{1}{s} \int_{t_1 - s/2}^{t_1 + s/2} [I_1(n) \cos 2\pi n t + I_2(n) \sin 2\pi n t] \, dt$$

$$= (1/2\pi n s)[I_1(n) \sin 2\pi n t - I_2(n) \cos 2\pi n t]_{t_1 - s/2}^{t_1 + s/2}$$

$$= (1/2\pi n s)\{I_1(n)[\sin 2\pi n(t_1 + s/2) - \sin 2\pi n(t_1 - s/2)]$$
$$\qquad - I_2(n)[\cos 2\pi n(t_1 + s/2) - \sin 2\pi n(t_1 - s/2)]\}$$

$$= (1/\pi n s)[I_1(n) \cos 2\pi n t_1 \sin 2\pi n s/2$$
$$\qquad\qquad + I_2(n) \sin 2\pi n t_1 \sin 2\pi n s/2]$$

$$= [(\sin \pi n s)/\pi n s][I_1(n) \cos 2\pi n t_1 + I_2(n) \sin 2\pi n t_1]$$

$$= [(\sin \pi n s)/\pi n s]u(t_1, n) \qquad\qquad (3.34)$$

In words, this means that the effect of the measuring instrument
averaging over a time interval s is to reduce the magnitude of the windspeed
at frequency n by a factor $(\sin \pi n s)/\pi n s$.

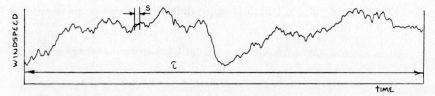

Fig. 3.10. Sample of the variation of windspeed with time defining averaging time and sample length.

The variance ($\sigma^2_{u,\infty,s}$) of an infinite sample of windspeed using this instrument is related to the spectral density function by the relationship

$$\sigma^2_{u,\infty,s} = \int_0^\infty S_{uu}(n)[(\sin \pi ns)/\pi ns]^2 \, \mathrm{d}n \qquad (3.35)$$

This has the same effect as a filter and is shown in Fig. 3.11.

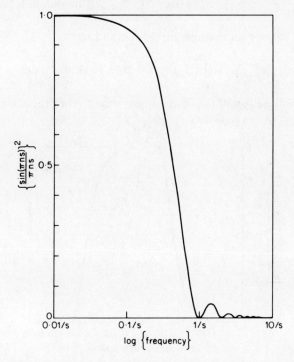

Fig. 3.11. Effect of averaging time of instrumentation on measured value of variance.

The effect of sample length is more difficult to explain, so it will be considered in steps.

(i)   The variance of a sample of length τ with zero averaging time is $\sigma^2_{u,\tau,0}$.

(ii) The variance of the means of an infinite number of such samples will be $\sigma^2_{u,\infty,\tau}$.

(iii) The variance of an infinite sample and zero averaging time $\sigma^2_{u,\infty,0}$ is related to the first two variances by the equation

$$\sigma^2_{u,\infty,0} = \sigma^2_{u,\infty,\tau} + [\sigma^2_{u,\tau,0}]_\infty \qquad (3.36)$$

where $[\;\;]_\infty$ means the average variance over the infinite number of samples.

Thus

$$[\sigma^2_{u,\tau,0}]_\infty = \sigma^2_{u,\infty,0} - \sigma^2_{u,\infty,\tau}$$

$$= \int_0^\infty S_{uu}(n)\,\mathrm{d}n - \int_0^\infty S_{uu}(n)\{(\sin \pi n\tau)/\pi n\tau\}^2\,\mathrm{d}n$$

by eqn. (3.35), for an averaging time of τ and not s.

$$[\sigma^2_{u,\tau,0}]_\infty = \int_0^\infty S_{uu}(n)\{1 - [(\sin \pi n\tau)/\pi n\tau]^2\}\,\mathrm{d}n \qquad (3.37)$$

which gives the effect of the finite sample length. The practical case is the combination of both effects.

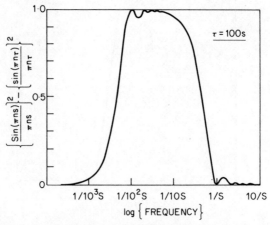

Fig. 3.12.   Effect of averaging time and sample length on measured value of variance.

Application of eqn. (3.36) and introducing the averaging time s,

$$\sigma^2_{u,\infty,s} = \sigma^2_{u,\infty,\tau} + [\sigma^2_{u,\tau,s}]_\infty$$

or

$$[\sigma^2_{u,\tau,s}]_\infty = \sigma^2_{u,\infty,s} - \sigma^2_{u,\infty,\tau}$$

and by substitution of eqn. (3.35) for both s and τ this gives

$$[\sigma^2_{u,\tau,s}]_\infty = \int_0^\infty S_{uu}(n)\{[(\sin \pi ns)/\pi ns]^2 - [(\sin \pi n\tau)/\pi n\tau]^2\}\,\mathrm{d}n \quad (3.38)$$

If it is assumed that the average variance over an infinite number of samples is the variance of the only sample measured, eqn. (3.38) represents the relationship between the measured variance and the true variance. This effect is identical to that of a filter; it is sometimes said that the effect of the limitations of the measurements can be represented by a window (shown in Fig. 3.12) through which the spectral density function is viewed.

3.11. Accuracy of Spectral Density Estimate

When estimating the spectral density function by means of a fast Fourier transform, it is essential to appreciate that the errors in the estimate at each frequency interval are of the order of the estimate, unless action is taken to reduce them.

The spectral density function is given by eqn. (3.9);

$$S_{uu}(n) = 1/T \int_0^T \frac{[I_1^2(n) + I_2^2(n)]}{2}\,\mathrm{d}t$$

where $I_1(n)$ and $I_2(n)$ for the FFT technique are given by eqns. (3.19). The differences from the mean values of $I_1(n)$ and $I_2(n)$ have a Gaussian distribution and the same variance, so that the spectral density function in eqn. (3.9) is the sum of the squares of two parts, each with a Gaussian distribution. The distribution of estimates of $S_{uu}(n)$ therefore follows a χ^2 distribution with two degrees of freedom. The mean value and variance are given by eqns. (2.17) and (2.18) to be n and $2n$. Consequently

$$\sigma[S_{uu}(n)]/S_{uu}(n) = (2n)^{1/2}/n = (2/n)^{1/2}$$

which is equal to unity for $n = 2$. This states that the standard deviation of the estimate is equal to the magnitude of the best estimate: obviously an unacceptable situation.

Two ways of improving the estimate must be used. The first is called 'ensemble averaging' and consists of taking a number of separate samples (increasing the length of the sample does not help as it only increases the frequency range covered), estimating $S_{uu}(n)$ from each sample individually and averaging the results. For every sample analysed the number of degrees of freedom increases by 2, so that for 25 samples the standard deviation of the estimate is 20% of the estimate. This is still not very good; increasing to 64 samples only increases σ to 12·5%. There is obviously a practical limit and it usually offers an error margin which is still unacceptable.

The second means whereby the error can be reduced is called 'frequency smoothing'. This means that estimates from adjacent frequencies are used to improve individual estimates. The bandwidth over which smoothing is performed must be chosen with care to ensure that no real data at discrete frequencies are removed.

The original proposition for this kind of smoothing was due to Hanning, whose window effectively replaced an estimate of $S_{uu}(n)$ by

$$\tfrac{1}{4}S_{uu}(n-1) + \tfrac{1}{2}S_{uu}(n) + \tfrac{1}{4}S_{uu}(n+1)$$

where $S_{uu}(n \pm 1)$ are the estimates of $S_{uu}(n)$ at the frequencies calculated on either side of $S_{uu}(n)$. Because this involves three estimates, it increases the number of degrees of freedom in the χ^2 distribution by a factor of approximately 3.

The author often finds this insufficient smoothing. To increase the bandwidth of the smoothing, more than three estimates can be involved. For instance, the odd binomial series can be used: $\tfrac{1}{16}, \tfrac{1}{4}, \tfrac{3}{8}, \tfrac{1}{4}, \tfrac{1}{16}$ or $\tfrac{1}{64}, \tfrac{3}{32}, \tfrac{15}{64}, \tfrac{5}{16}, \tfrac{15}{64}, \tfrac{3}{32}, \tfrac{1}{64}$. In these latter cases, because only a small fraction of the extreme values are added, it would not be reasonable to assume that the variances of all the series in the χ^2 distribution were the same. It is difficult to give an exact number of degrees of freedom to be used in each case; a value of $1·5N$, where N is the number of terms, gives some idea of the effect. Thus the effect of a seventh-order series would give a reduction in the standard deviation of the estimate to between $\tfrac{1}{3}$ and $\tfrac{1}{4}$.

Thus the combination of using 25 samples and employing a seventh-order smoothing curve would be to reduce the standard deviation of the estimate to about 5% of the estimate: about as far as it is practical to go.

If the spectral density function is known to be a smooth function of frequency, and the spectrum even after ensemble averaging and frequency smoothing is still spiky, a smoother curve will be obtained by a second smoothing process (often taking straight averages of N consecutive readings) than by increasing the order of the one and only smoothing process.

4

Statistics: Extension of Covariance and Spectral Density Functions to Consider Two Components of Windspeed or Two Points in Space

In the last chapter all the quantities related to windspeed at one location. The concept of correlation lends itself to the inter-relationship of two components and to values at two locations. This extension, though basically simple, introduces some complications and involves some additional definitions. Combinations of two components are considered in Sections 4.1 to 4.4, and of two locations thereafter.

4.1. COVARIANCE

This term is akin to the variance of a single variable and consequently its symbol is similar:

$$\sigma_{uv}^2 = \overline{u(t)v(t)} \tag{4.1}$$

4.2. CROSS COVARIANCE FUNCTION

This term is akin to the autocovariance function and is defined as

$$C_{uv}(\tau) = \overline{u(t)v(t + \tau)} \tag{4.2}$$

and the appropriate cross covariance coefficient

$$c_{uv}(\tau) = C_{uv}(\tau)/(\sigma_u \sigma_v) \tag{4.3}$$

An additional complication now arises, as the cross covariance function is no longer symmetrical with respect to τ and integrations have to be made from $-\infty$ to $+\infty$.

61

4.3. CROSS SPECTRAL DENSITY FUNCTION

In the derivation of the relationship between the autocovariance and
spectral density functions (eqn. (3.16)) the cross-terms vanished; in this
instance they do not, and eqn. (3.17) has to be replaced by

$$S_{uv}(n) = 2 \int_{-\infty}^{\infty} C_{uv}(\tau) \exp(-i2\pi n\tau)\, d\tau \tag{4.4}$$

$$= P_{uv}(n) - iQ_{uv}(n) \tag{4.5}$$

where $P_{uv}(n)$ is called the 'cospectrum' and $Q_{uv}(n)$ is called the
'quadspectrum', and these are related to the cross covariance function:

$$P_{uv}(n) = 2 \int_{0}^{\infty} [C_{uv}(\tau) + C_{uv}(-\tau)] \cos 2\pi n\tau\, d\tau \tag{4.6}$$

$$Q_{uv}(n) = 2 \int_{0}^{\infty} [C_{uv}(\tau) - C_{uv}(-\tau)] \sin 2\pi n\tau\, d\tau \tag{4.7}$$

Sometimes $C_{uv}(-\tau)$ is written as $C_{vu}(\tau)$. At other times the cross covariance

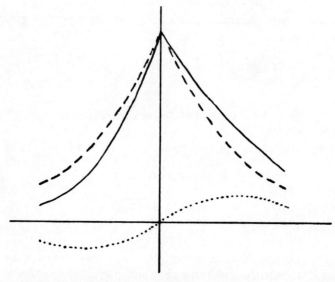

Fig. 4.1. Breakdown of cross covariance function into symmetric and antisymmetric parts.

function is divided into a symmetrical and an antisymmetrical part shown in Fig. 4.1, instead of $+\tau$ and $-\tau$ parts. Thus

$$2C_{uv}(\tau)_{\text{sym}} = C_{uv}(\tau) + C_{uv}(-\tau)$$

and

$$2C_{vv}(\tau)_{\text{antisym}} = C_{uv}(\tau) - C_{uv}(-\tau)$$

This means that eqns. (4.6) and (4.7) can be rewritten

$$P_{uv}(n) = 4 \int_0^\infty C_{uv}(\tau)_{\text{sym}} \cos 2\pi n\tau \, d\tau \qquad (4.6a)$$

and

$$Q_{uv}(n) = 4 \int_0^\infty C_{uv}(\tau)_{\text{antisym}} \sin 2\pi n\tau \, d\tau \qquad (4.7a)$$

The polar form can be used for the cross spectral density function in which

$$S_{uv}(n) = [|S_{uv}(n)|] \exp [i\theta_{uv}(n)] \qquad (4.8)$$

where $|S_{uv}(n)|$ is called the modulus or absolute magnitude of the cross spectral density function and $\theta_{uv}(n)$ is called the phase angle. These quantities are related to the cospectrum and the quadspectrum by the expressions

$$[|S_{uv}(n)|]^2 = P_{uv}^2(n) + Q_{uv}^2(n) \qquad (4.9)$$

and

$$\theta_{uv}(n) = \tan^{-1} [Q_{uv}(n)/P_{uv}(n)] \qquad (4.10)$$

4.4. COHERENCE FUNCTION

Just as it is convenient in certain circumstances to have an autocovariance coefficient as well as a function, the coefficient associated with the cross spectral density function is called a coherence function:

$$\gamma_{uv}^2(n) = [|S_{uv}(n)|]^2/[S_{uu}(n)S_{vv}(n)] \qquad (4.11)$$

4.5. SPATIAL COVARIANCE

The variance of one variable, the covariance of two components of the windspeed at one location and the spatial covariance of a windspeed at two locations form a sequence. Thus the spatial covariance is defined:

$$\sigma_{uu'}^2 = \overline{u(t,r)u(t,r^1)} \tag{4.12}$$

where $r(x,y,z)$ and $r^1(x^1 y^1 z^1)$ represent the two locations at which measurements were taken.

4.6. Spatial Covariance Function

Following the sequence, the spatial covariance function relates the windspeed at two locations at different times. Thus

$$C_{uu'}(\tau) = \overline{u(t,r)u(t+\tau,r^1)} \tag{4.13}$$

4.7. Spatial Spectrum Density Function

In a similar vein

$$S_{uu'}(n) = 2\int_{-\infty}^{\infty} C_{uu'}(\tau)\exp(-i2\pi n\tau)\,d\tau \tag{4.14}$$

and similar definitions occur for spatial cospectrum, spatial quadspectrum, spatial modulus, spatial phase angle and spatial coherence function.

4.8. Expressions for Different Components of Windspeed at Two Locations

The cross spatial covariance, cross spatial covariance function, cross spatial spectral density function and their derivatives are defined in the obvious way.

4.9. Integral Length Scales

The concept of a single length which, in some way, represents an average turbulence length in the windspeed has great attraction. In Section 3.1 the similar concept of an integral time was described. Because windspeed has three components and there are three directions over which to measure the length, there will be nine integral scale lengths. There is difficulty in devising a symbol for these: the integral scale in the x direction relating to the u component of velocity used to be called $L_u(x)$. This is a poor symbol because this scale length is not a function of x; it is a measurement in the x

direction. The Engineering Sciences Data Unit solved this problem by the cumbersome symbol ^xL_u in all its Data Items and the same symbols will be used in these volumes. Thus

$$^xL_u = \int_0^\infty \{\sigma_{uu'}^2 / \sigma_u^2\} \, \mathrm{d}x \qquad (4.15)$$

where $\sigma_{uu'}$ is given by

$$\sigma_{uu'}^2 = \overline{u(t, x)u(t, x + \delta x)}$$

The other eight integral scale lengths are calculated in a similar fashion.

The measurement of integral length scales requires the simultaneous measurement at two locations, necessitating two complete sets of measuring instruments. Some experimenters invoke Taylor's Hypothesis which incorporates the idea of a turbulence pattern 'frozen' into the wind so that, along the direction of mean wind, time and distance can be exchanged with reference to the mean windspeed. Thus

$$^xL_u = T_u \bar{U} \qquad (4.16)$$

where T_u is defined in the next section. It is recommended that this relationship is used with great care.

4.10. INTEGRAL TIME SCALES

Equation (3.7) in Section 3.1 introduced an integral time scale for the windspeed (T_u). When components of windspeed are concerned there are three time scales relating to the three components. Thus

$$T_u = \int_0^\infty c_{uu}(\tau) \, \mathrm{d}\tau \qquad (4.17)$$

But by eqn. (3.17)

$$S_{uu}(n) = 4 \int_0^\infty C_{uu}(\tau) \cos 2\pi n\tau \, \mathrm{d}\tau$$

Therefore

$$T_u = \tfrac{1}{4} S_{uu}(0) \qquad (4.18)$$

It follows that, if the mean value has been removed by an analogue high-pass filter at a frequency higher than the resolution bandwidth,

$$S_{uu}(0) = 0$$
$$T_u = 0$$

5

Statistics: Extreme Value Analysis

In design work the greatest load that a member has to withstand during its lifetime is required for insertion into the calculations of the strength of the member. This is easy to calculate when the system is deterministic but appears impossible for random data, especially when the time interval over which the maximum value is to be calculated is longer than the period over which measurements have been made.

As magnitudes are required, and as these are expressed in terms of the probability density function or its integral, it is to these functions that we turn. To try to avoid confusion, the variable will be called x in the parent distribution and X in the extreme value distribution.

5.1. The Three Possible Types of Extreme Value Distribution

Suppose the population of data were split into N samples, each containing n readings. When each sample is scanned it will be found to have a largest reading, and the largest reading in the population will be the largest reading in one of the samples. Consequently, the distribution of the largest values in the population will tend to the same asymptotic value as the distribution of just the largest value in each of the N samples.

It is obvious that this statement is not exact and that there will be occasions when the second largest value in one sample will be larger than the largest in another sample. The Monte Carlo method deals with this situation and is mentioned in Section 4.7 of Volume 1. In this paragraph the 'tendency' will be accepted.

The assumption is implied in Section 5.1 that n is infinite; Section 5.8 discusses the extension of the theory for a finite value of n.

Equation (2.39) states that if $P_1(x_0)$ is the probability that the value of x

is smaller than x_0 in a sample, the probability that the value of x is smaller than X_0 in N samples is given by $P(X_0)$, where

$$P(X_0) = [P_1(x_0)]^N$$

by the binomial distribution. Because a linear transformation of the variable is shown by eqn. (2.11) not to change the form of the distribution, this relationship can be rewritten

$$P_N[a(N)X_0 + b(N)] = P_1(x_0) \tag{5.1}$$

where the LHS applies to the extreme value distribution, and $a(N)$ and $b(N)$ are constants dependent upon the number of samples N.

When $a(N) = 1$, eqn. (5.1) can be rewritten

$$P_N[X_0 + b(N)] = P_1(x_0) \tag{5.2}$$

This represents only a linear shift of $b(N)$ in the value of the variable, the two distributions being parallel. This equation has the two unknowns $b(N)$ and $P(X)$ and these can be determined (see a textbook on statistics or Gumbel [21], pages 158 *et seq.*) in the limit as $n \to \infty$

$$P(X_0) = \exp\{-\exp[-\alpha(X_0 - U)]\} \tag{5.3}$$

where U and α are constants independent of N.

For eqns. (5.2) and (5.3) to be satisfied simultaneously

$$b(N) = -\{\ln N\}/\alpha \tag{5.4}$$

The solution is called 'the first asymptote' by Gumbel and is identical to an earlier derivation by Fisher and Tippett, which they called a type-I solution.

When $a(N) \neq 1$, the two distributions $P^N(x)$ and $P[a(N)X + b(N)]$ are no longer parallel, but there will be a value x_1 at which the two probabilities are equal, i.e.

$$X_1 = x_1 = b(N)/[1 - a(N)] \tag{5.5}$$

so that

$$P^N(x_1) \doteq P(X_1)$$

which can only be satisfied if $P(X_1) = 0$ or 1.

These conditions lead to the second asymptotic (type-II) condition when $P(x_1) = 0$ and the third asymptotic (type-III) condition when $P(X_1) = 1$.

In the type-II condition, the solution is bounded by $X > X_1$ so we can perform a linear transformation with no change in function so that $X_1 = 0$.

By eqn. (5.5) this means that $b(N) = 0$ and eqn. (5.1) can be rewritten

$$P^N(x) = P[a(N)X]$$

By arguments similar to those used in the type-I solution, the cumulative density function is found to be

$$P(X) = \exp[-(v/X)^k] \qquad (5.6)$$

where $x \geq 0$, $v > 0$ and $k > 0$, and the value of $a(N)$ is given by

$$a(N) = N^{-1/k} \qquad (5.7)$$

In the type-III condition the solution is bounded by $X < X_1$ and by a linear shift so that all values of X are negative, producing the cumulative distribution function

$$P(X) = \exp[-(X/v)^k] \qquad (5.8)$$

where $x \leq 0$, $v < 0$, $k > 0$ and the value of $a(N)$ is given by

$$a(N) = N^{1/k} \qquad (5.9)$$

5.2. CHOICE OF EXTREME VALUE DISTRIBUTION FOR A GIVEN PARENT DISTRIBUTION

The type-I distribution applies to all parent distributions of the form

$$P(x) = 1 - \exp[-g(x)] \qquad (5.10)$$

where $g(x)$ is a monotonic function of x. The Gaussian, log normal, binomial, Rayleigh and Weibull distributions are all of this type.

The type-II distribution applies to all parent distributions of the form

$$P(x) = 1 - \beta(1 - x)^k \qquad (5.11)$$

where $x \geq 0$.

The type-III distribution applies to all parent distributions of the form

$$P(x) = 1 - \gamma(-x)^k \qquad (5.12)$$

where $x \leq 0$.

5.3. FISHER–TIPPETT TYPE-I DISTRIBUTION

As this applies to most distributions, it is worth further consideration. Following Gumbel, eqn. (5.3) is often rewritten

$$P(X) = \exp[-\exp(-y)] \qquad (5.13)$$

where

$$y = \alpha(X - U) \tag{5.14}$$

and is called the reduced variate. α is called the dispersion and U the mode of the data.

Differentiation of eqn. (5.13) gives the probability density function for this distribution:

$$p(X) = \alpha \exp(-y) \exp[-\exp(-y)] \tag{5.15}$$

5.4. RETURN PERIOD

It is convenient to specify a period of time within which an occurrence is required not to happen. In building aerodynamics most codes of practice use a return period of 50 years.

By the definition of the return period T, the probability that the value x_0 will be exceeded in one sample is $1/T$, so that

$$P_1(x_0) = 1 - 1/T$$

It therefore follows from eqn. (2.39) that the probability that the same value X_0 will not be exceeded in T samples will be

$$P_T(X_0) = [P_1(x_0)]^T = [1 - (1/T)]^T \tag{5.16}$$

Sometimes the value of

$$Q_T(X_0) = 1 - P_T(X_0)$$

is erroneously quoted as the probability that the value X_0 will be exceeded once in T samples, whereas it also includes the probability that the value X_0 will be exceeded many times in the T samples.

5.5. ESTIMATION OF AN EXTREME VALUE KNOWING THE LARGEST VALUE FROM A NUMBER OF SAMPLES

This procedure follows the derivation of the extreme value distribution in Section 5.1. Suppose that the population is divided into N samples, each containing n readings. The largest value from each sample is given a rank M such that $M = 1$ represents the lowest largest value and $M = N$ represents the highest.

The cumulative distribution function for the Mth highest value

$$P(X_M) = M/(N + 1) \qquad (5.16a)$$

which by eqn. (5.13) is equal to

$$M/(N + 1) = \exp\left[-\exp\left(-y_M\right)\right]$$

or

$$y_M = -\ln\left\{-\ln\left[M/(N + 1)\right]\right\} \qquad (5.17)$$

where

$$y_M = \alpha(X_M - U) \qquad (5.18)$$

and X_M is the Mth largest value.

It is conventional to plot X as ordinate and y as abscissa (see Fig. 5.1).

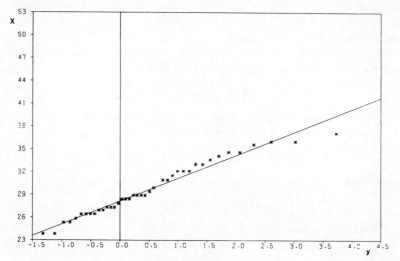

Fig. 5.1. Variation of annual maximum windspeeds with reduced variate.

Equation (5.19) suggests that a straight line can be drawn through the points. The equation of this line is often determined by the method of least squares (see Section 6.6) and values of α and U are derived from this straight line.

Due to the fact that the estimation of the cumulative distribution function in eqn. (5.16a) is biased in the statistical sense (and the least squares method involving equal weighting of all readings does nothing to reduce the bias) some inaccuracies are introduced by this method. Leiblein [28] has produced sets of linear unbiased estimators and has found a set which produces the 'most efficient' results (based on the Gamer–Rao definition of efficiency). This set is called the 'best linear unbiased estimators' (BLUE). Implementation of the BLUE on a digital computer provides both increased efficiency and reduced computer time (provided the coefficients for the particular application are in the computer memory) over the least squares method and is preferred. The BLUE method is described in Section 6.7.

It is now possible to determine the extreme value within the return period T described in the last paragraph:

$$P_1(x_0) = 1 - 1/T$$

and by eqn. (5.17)

$$y_T = -\ln\{-\ln[P_1(X_0)]\} = -\ln\{-\ln[1 - 1/T]\} \qquad (5.19)$$

and

$$X_T = U + y_T/\alpha \qquad (5.19a)$$

5.6. Estimation of an Extreme Value Knowing the Parent Distribution

For those distributions for which the type-I extreme value distribution applies (see Section 5.2), the cumulative distribution function will be given by eqn. (5.10), viz.

$$P(x) = 1 - \exp[-g(x)]$$

If only one sample of n readings has been taken, then it follows that the largest reading in that one sample will be the most likely reading in the extreme value distribution, which by definition is the modal value U. Thus from eqn. (5.10)

$$1 - 1/n = P(U) = 1 - \exp[-g(U)]$$

from which

$$g(U) = +\ln n \qquad (5.20)$$

The expressions can be expanded as a Taylor's series and all higher terms ignored if

$$g''(U) \ll g(U)$$

which gives a simple expression for the dispersion

$$\alpha = g'(U) \qquad (5.21)$$

This follows a method due to Cramer [9], to which reference the reader is referred for further details.

In practice this means that, should the parent distribution be known, it is possible to determine the constants U from eqn. (5.20) and α from eqn. (5.21). But a word of warning about the number of readings n in the sample is given in the next section.

5.7. NUMBER OF INDEPENDENT READINGS

When a continuously varying quantity is digitised to produce the n readings in the sample considered above, all the readings are not necessarily independent. If some part of the physical system involved contained a sizable variation of much lower frequency than the digitisation rate, then series of consecutive readings would be either high or low depending upon the phase of the low-frequency component. So periodically throughout the sample there would exist families of high readings which could in no sense be considered independent. As most statistical analysis presupposes that all the readings are independent, false conclusions would be drawn if they were not. In particular, an incorrect value for n in the last section would ensure incorrect values for the mode and dispersion of the extreme value distribution.

In work by Rice [43] a cycling or up-crossing rate parameter v has been defined from the spectral density function $S(n)$ such that

$$v = \left[\int_0^\infty n^2 S_{uu}(n)\,\mathrm{d}n \middle/ \int_0^\infty S_{uu}(n)\,\mathrm{d}n \right]^{1/2} \tag{5.22}$$

This gives a reasonable estimate of the frequency of independent readings which can be taken from the sample. When the *duration* of the sample is T, then the maximum number of independent readings which could be obtained is

$$n_{\max} = vT \tag{5.23}$$

The recommended procedure is to use the number of samples measured (n) when the digitisation rate is less than v. When the digitisation rate is greater than v, then the number of readings used in Section 5.6 ought to equal n_e, where n_e is given either by eqn. (5.23) or by

$$n_e = n v/(\text{digitisation rate}) \tag{5.24}$$

whichever is less. When applied to measurements of windspeed and surface pressure on models of buildings in a wind tunnel, Gomes and Vickery have shown that the above method tends to underestimate the values of U and α even when the value of n_e is used with eqns. (5.20) and (5.21). Their work applies only to a parent distribution of the Weibull type (see Section 2.9) and they recommend that the values of U and α are multiplied by factors in the curly brackets so that they become

$$U = c(\ln n_e)^{1/k}\{1 + (k - 1)[\ln(\ln n_e)]/(k^2 \ln n_e)\} \qquad (5.25)$$

and

$$1/\alpha = (c/k)(\ln n_e)^{(1-k)/k}$$
$$\times \{1 + (k - 1)/(k \ln n_e) - (k - 1)^2[\ln(\ln n_e)]/(k^2 \ln n_e)\} \qquad (5.26)$$

5.8. EXTREME VALUES IN A SAMPLE OF FINITE SIZE

The preceding paragraphs have considered asymptotic values (Gumbel calls the three solutions first, second and third asymptotes) which assume samples of infinite size. Most samples of interest are of limited size or duration so the theory must be amended to suit this type of problem.

As with the different approaches to the asymptotic values (Sections 5.5 and 5.6) there are two different approaches when the sample size is limited.

When the cumulative distribution function of the parent distribution is known in closed form, the following approach is possible and will be explained using two examples.

For a Rayleigh distribution of the parent data, the cumulative distribution function is given by

$$P(x) = 1 - \exp[-(x/c)^2]$$

where

$$c = 2\sigma_x/(4 - \pi)^{1/2}$$

so that the modal value for samples of the parent data containing n readings would be

$$1/n = \exp[-(U/c)^2]$$

or

$$U = c\sqrt{\ln n} = 2\sigma_x(\ln n)^{1/2}/(4 - \pi)^{1/2}$$
$$= 1{\cdot}526\sigma_x(2\ln n)^{1/2}$$

or, by eqn. (5.21),

$$g(x) = (x/c)^2 \qquad g'(x) = 2x/c^2$$
$$\alpha = g'(U) = 2(\ln n)^{1/2}/c = 0{\cdot}9265(\ln n)^{1/2}/\sigma_x$$

The median value of the extreme value distribution can be calculated from eqn. (5.3):

$$P(X_{median}) = 0 \cdot 5 = \exp \{ -\exp [-\alpha(X_{median} - U)] \}$$

or

$$X_{median} = U - \ln [-\ln (0 \cdot 5)] / \alpha$$

or

$$X_{median}/\sigma_x = U/\sigma_x + 0 \cdot 5595/(2 \ln n)^{1/2}$$
$$= 1 \cdot 526(2 \ln n)^{1/2} + 0 \cdot 5595/(2 \ln n)^{1/2} \qquad (5.27)$$

and

$$U/\sigma_x = 1 \cdot 526(2 \ln n)^{1/2} \qquad (5.28)$$

To show the effect of the different parent distributions on these values a second example, for an exponential distribution, will now be evaluated.

$$P(x) = 1 - \exp [-(x/\sigma_x)]$$
$$1/n = \exp [-(U/\sigma_x)]$$
$$U = \sigma_x \ln n$$
$$\alpha = 1/\sigma_x$$
$$U/\sigma_x = \ln n \qquad (5.29)$$

$$X_{median}/\sigma_x = \ln n + 0 \cdot 3665 \qquad (5.30)$$

For parent distributions for which the cumulative distribution function is not known in closed form, a different approach is required. In this case the usual approach is to revert to the method of Section 5.5 and to start with the cumulative distribution function for the extreme values, assuming that the extreme values from N samples have already been extracted.

Equation (5.3) gives

$$p(X) = \exp \{ -\exp [-\alpha(X - U)] \}$$

Gumbel [21] shows that the mean value and standard deviation of this distribution are

$$\bar{X} = U + 0 \cdot 5772/\alpha \qquad (5.31)$$

and

$$S_x = \pi/\sqrt{6}\alpha \qquad (5.32)$$

and that these values can be calculated from the extreme values of the N samples in the usual way:

$$\bar{X} = (1/N) \sum_{i=1}^{N} X_i \qquad (5.33)$$

$$S_x^2 = [1/(N-1)] \sum_{i=1}^{N} (X_i - \bar{X})^2 \qquad (5.34)$$

By substituting for α from eqn. (5.32) into eqn. (5.31), the value of the mode is obtained as

$$U/S_x = \bar{X}/S_x - 0{\cdot}4500 \qquad (5.35)$$

and the median value is obtained by eqn. (5.3):

$$P(X_{\text{median}}) = 0{\cdot}5 = \exp\{-\exp[-\alpha(X_{\text{median}} - U)]\}$$

or

$$X_{\text{median}}/S_x = U/S_x + 0{\cdot}2858 \qquad (5.36)$$

where $\bar{X}$ and S_x have been calculated by eqns. (5.33) and (5.34).

It follows from eqn. (5.19) that the extreme value X_T which has probability $P_T(X_T)$ of occurring in T samples is given by

$$\begin{aligned} X_T &= U + y_T/\alpha \\ &= \bar{X} + (y_T - 0{\cdot}5772)0{\cdot}7797S_x \end{aligned} \qquad (5.37)$$

where

$$y_T = -\ln\{-\ln[1 - 1/T]\}$$

Gumbel has studied the variation of values of X at a given value of y and finds that the distribution is Gaussian with a standard deviation approximating to

$$\sigma_{x_1}^2 = [1 + 0{\cdot}8885(y - 0{\cdot}5772) + 0{\cdot}6687(y - 0{\cdot}5772)^2]S_x^2/N \qquad (5.38)$$

where N is the number of extreme values used in the analysis.

This expression can be reduced to

$$\sigma_x^2 = (0{\cdot}2643 + 0{\cdot}1166y + 0{\cdot}6687y^2)S_x^2/N \qquad (5.39)$$

By substitution of eqn. (5.37) into (5.38), eqn. (5.39) becomes

$$\sigma_x^2 = [S_x^2 + 1{\cdot}1396S_x(X - \bar{X}) + 1{\cdot}1(X - \bar{X})^2]/N$$

which for the mean value of X, i.e. $X = \bar{X}$, reduces to

$$\sigma_{\bar{x}}^2 = S_x^2/N$$

which is the same as eqn. (6.4). The form most useful to apply is that given by eqn. (5.39) because it allows the variance of X to be calculated at any value of y.

Gumbel also showed that the distribution was Gaussian, so that at any value of the reduced variate y, it would be expected that 68 % of all readings were within the limits

$$\bar{X} + (y - 0{\cdot}5772)0{\cdot}7797S_x \pm \sigma_x$$

that 95 % of all readings were within the limits

$$\bar{X} + (y - 0{\cdot}5772)0{\cdot}7797S_x \pm 2\sigma_x$$

and 99·7 % of all readings between the limits

$$\bar{X} + (y - 0{\cdot}5772)0{\cdot}7797S_x \pm 3\sigma_x$$

5.9. Confidence Levels and Intervals

It follows directly from the last section that it is possible to quote with stated confidence a range of values of X within which the true value of X will lie.

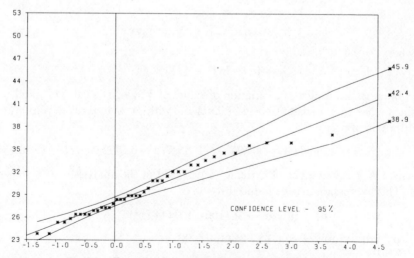

Fig. 5.2. Extreme value analysis showing confidence level lines.

The confidence level is the percentage of values expected between the limits, and the confidence interval is equal to the increment on either side of the best-fit line within which the true value is stated to lie with that confidence. It is obvious that the greater the confidence level, the greater the confidence interval.

The confidence level is defined by the equation

$$\text{confidence level (in \%)}/100 = 2 \int_0^k \exp\left(-z^2/2\right) dz \qquad (5.40)$$

from which the value of k is calculated. The confidence interval follows from eqn. (2.13) as $\pm k\sigma_x$, where σ_x is calculated by eqn. (5.39) for the appropriate value of y. These lines are shown for a confidence level of 95 % on wind data in Fig. 5.2.

5.10. Possible Discard of Highest Values

When extreme value analysis is applied to meteorological measurements of windspeed of limited duration, a problem can occur in the interpretation of the data because of the chronological order in which the data were obtained. For example, the largest reading in 100 years of data can occur during the first 10 years (it could even occur during the first year, but nobody would carry out an extreme value analysis upon one reading). If this happened and a best-fit line were drawn through the ten points, it would be found that:

(i)   the line was not a good straight line;
(ii) the largest reading would distort the line so that it did not follow the trend of the data.

In Fig. 5.3 the maximum annual gusts at Cranwell are presented in the usual way for a record covering 42 years. The largest windspeed of $49 \cdot 3 \text{ m s}^{-1}$ occurred on 17 December 1952 and the best-fit line with the 95 % confidence level lines also shown excludes this value. Recomputation with this value eliminated (Fig. 5.2) shows much better agreement with the data and would suggest that the event of 17 December 1952 was a once-in-1153-years occurrence or would be within the 95 % confidence levels in 366 years. It is also possible that this event was part of a different population which had a very low probability of occurrence, so that it would not be expected more than once in the 42 years of records. To ascertain whether this was so, a study must be made of the synoptic condition at Cranwell on that day and

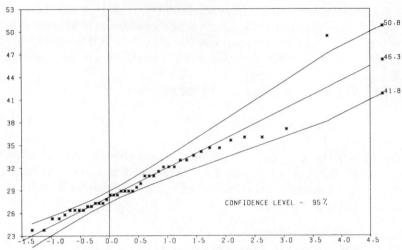

Fig. 5.3.   Extreme value analysis containing one very unusual occurrence.

if some very unusual weather condition was present, then the techniques used for mixed populations and described in the next section should be used.

5.11.   MIXED POPULATIONS

There may be two or more completely separate mechanisms afoot which are responsible for the values of the quantity measured. For example, if our variable is windspeed, in temperate latitudes there is a single mechanism due to uneven heating of the atmosphere and its subsequent reorganisation by the rotation of the earth. In this case the preceding paragraphs apply. In parts of world where tropical cyclones or tornadoes occur, however, there are additional mechanisms which often produce very high windspeeds. A further complication arises in that some of these phenomena are of small size and consequently only affect a small area of land, and even then the effects vary rapidly with distance.

This means that three aspects must be considered—firstly, the probability of extreme winds due to the usual mechanism; secondly, the winds caused by the tornado (for example); and thirdly, the probability that the path of the tornado will be sufficiently close to the site to have an appreciable effect. This is a rather specialist aspect and will be considered again in Section 7.5.

Thom [47] has proposed that the distribution for a mixed population can be represented by the addition of two cumulative distribution functions, where the factors F_1 and F_2 are the probabilities that mechanisms 1 and 2 will produce the maximum value in a sample:

$$P(X) = F_1 \exp\left[-\exp\left(-y_1\right)\right] + F_2 \exp\left[-\exp\left(-y_2\right)\right] \qquad (5.41)$$

assuming that both mechanisms produce parent distributions which satisfy the type-I extreme value distribution, and the reduced variates y_1 and y_2 have different modes and dispersions.

6

Statistics: Confidence Intervals and Linear Regression

Statistics can be applied in an attempt to reduce random experimental errors in the measurement of static quantities, and to produce best estimates and limits between which the value can be predicted to lie with a given confidence. They can also be used to determine whether the difference between two measurements of a quantity is significant, and to establish variations in mathematical form.

6.1. BEST ESTIMATE OF A STATIC QUANTITY

When a static quantity is measured N times the mean value of all the readings is called the mean value of the sample ($\bar{x}$). So

$$\bar{x} = (1/N) \sum_{i=1}^{N} x_i \qquad (6.1)$$

The true mean value μ is the mean value from an infinite population. However, the sample mean is the best estimate of the true mean. This is sometimes written

$$\bar{x} = E(\mu) \qquad (6.2)$$

The variance of the sample (s^2) would at first glance appear to be

$$s^2 = (1/N) \sum_{i=1}^{N} (x_i - \bar{x})^2$$

but Bessell has shown that there is bias in this estimate and that the best estimate of variance from a sample of N readings is

$$s^2 = [1/(N-1)] \sum_{i=1}^{N} (x_i - \bar{x})^2 \tag{6.3}$$

Suppose the mean value were measured in N samples, each containing N readings. This could be written

$$\bar{x}_1 = (1/N)(_1x_1 + {}_1x_2 + {}_1x_3 + \cdots {}_1x_N)$$
$$\bar{x}_2 = (1/N)(_2x_1 + {}_2x_2 + {}_2x_3 + \cdots {}_2x_N)$$

until

$$\bar{x}_N = (1/N)(_Nx_1 + {}_Nx_2 + {}_Nx_3 + \cdots {}_Nx_N)$$

It follows by addition that the variance of the mean is equal to the variance of individual readings divided by N. Thus

$$\sigma_{\bar{x}} = \sigma_x / \sqrt{N} \tag{6.4}$$

6.2. CONFIDENCE INTERVALS

6.2.1. *Mean with Known Variance*

The evaluation of the mean value is given by eqn. (6.1). Provided that all errors are random, the distribution of the values of x about $\bar{x}$ will follow the Gaussian distribution described in Section 2.5, and the probability density function of eqn. (2.12) applies.

However, to use tabulated results it is better to transform into the variable z, where

$$z = (x - \bar{x})/\sigma_x \tag{6.5}$$

It is convenient at this stage to introduce a shorthand notation used in tables. The value of z for which the cumulative distribution function is equal to $\alpha/2$ is called $z_{\alpha/2}$, or in mathematical terminology

$$\text{Prob}\,[z > z_{\alpha/2}] = Q(z_{\alpha/2}) = \alpha/2 \tag{6.6}$$

Thus the probability that the true mean value μ lies between the values $\bar{x} - \sigma_x z_{\alpha/2}/\sqrt{N}$ and $\bar{x} + \sigma_x z_{\alpha/2}/\sqrt{N}$ is $(1 - \alpha)$. Or, again in mathematical terminology,

$$\text{Prob}\,[\bar{x} - \sigma_x z_{\alpha/2}/\sqrt{N} \le \mu < \bar{x} + \sigma_x z_{\alpha/2}/\sqrt{N}] = (1 - \alpha) \tag{6.7}$$

The difference between the values $\pm\sigma_x z_{\alpha/2}/\sqrt{N}$ is called the confidence interval, and $(1 - \alpha)$ is called the confidence coefficient.

The statement is often made in these terms: 'There is $(1 - \alpha)$ confidence that the true value of $\bar{x}$ lies between these limits'.

If the variance is not known but only estimated, then Section 6.2.3 applies.

6.2.2. *Variance (or Standard Deviation)*

The best estimate of the variance is given by eqn. (6.3):

$$s^2 = [1/(N-1)]\sum_{i=1}^{N}(x_i - \bar{x})^2$$

$$= [1/(N-1)]\left[\sum_{i=1}^{N}(x_i - \mu)^2 - N(\bar{x} - \mu)^2\right]$$

$$= [1/(N-1)]\left[\sigma_x^2\sum_{i=1}^{N}z_i^2 - \frac{N\sigma_x^2 z^2}{N}\right]$$

$$= [1/(N-1)]\sigma_x^2\sum_{i=1}^{N-1}z_i^2$$

$$= [1/(N-1)]\sigma_x^2\chi_{N-1}^2$$

or

$$\chi_{N-1}^2 = s^2(N-1)/\sigma_x^2$$

or

$$s^2 = \{\chi_{N-1}^2\sigma_x^2\}/(N-1)$$

$$\text{Prob}\,[(N-1)s^2/\chi_{N-1;\alpha/2}^2 < \sigma^2 < (N-1)s^2\chi_{N-1;1-\alpha/2}^2] = (1-\alpha)$$

where

$$\text{Prob}\,[\chi_N^2 > \chi_{N;\alpha}^2] = \alpha \qquad (6.8)$$

The physical reason why the number of degrees of freedom is $(N-1)$ is that one has been used to calculate the mean value.

6.2.3. *Mean with Sample Variance Only*

The sample mean $(\bar{x})$ is calculated from eqn. (6.1). If s is the sample standard deviation, then the sample standard deviation for mean values by eqn. (6.4) is $s/\sqrt{N}$. The variable whose distribution we want is

$$\frac{\bar{x} - \mu}{s/\sqrt{N}} = \frac{z\sigma_{\bar{x}}}{s/\sqrt{N}} \qquad \text{by Section 6.2.1}$$

$$= \frac{z\sigma_x/\sqrt{N}}{s/\sqrt{N}} \qquad \text{by eqn. (6.4)}$$

$$= \frac{z\sigma_x}{\sigma_x\chi_{N-1}/(N-1)^{1/2}} \qquad \text{by eqn. (6.8)}$$

$$= \frac{z}{\sqrt{\chi_{N-1}^2/(N-1)}}$$

$$= t_{N-1} \qquad \text{by eqn. (2.21)}$$

Thus

$$\text{Prob}\,[\bar{x} - st_{N-1;\alpha/2}/\sqrt{N} \leq \mu < \bar{x} + st_{N-1;\alpha/2}] = (1 - \alpha) \qquad (6.9)$$

where

$$\text{Prob}\,[t_N > t_{N,\alpha}] = \alpha \qquad (6.10)$$

6.2.4. *The Ratio of Two Sample Variances*

$$\frac{s_x^2/\sigma_x^2}{s_y^2/\sigma_y^2} = \frac{\sigma_x^2\chi_{n_x}^2/n_x\sigma_x^2}{\sigma_y^2\chi_{n_y}^2/n_y\sigma_y^2} = \frac{\chi_{n_x}^2/n_x}{\chi_{n_y}^2/n_y} = F_{n_x n_y}$$

where

$$n_x = N_x - 1$$

and

$$n_y = N_y - 1$$

Thus

$$\text{Prob}\,[s_x^2 s_y^2 > \{\sigma_x^2/\sigma_y^2\}F_{n_x;n_y;\alpha}] = \alpha \qquad (6.11)$$

where the F distribution is given in Section 2.13.

6.3. HYPOTHESIS TESTS

These are used to determine whether two sets of measurements are significantly different. They usually start with a *null hypothesis*. This postulates that all the measurements are from the same population.

Suppose in the first set of measurements n_1 readings were taken, and the mean value and standard deviation were $\bar{x}_1$ and s_1 given by eqns. (6.1) and (6.3) respectively. In the second set of measurements n_2 readings were taken and the values were $\bar{x}_2$ and s_2.

Two possible errors can be made: they are a *type-1 error*, when the hypothesis is rejected when it is true, and a *type-2 error*, when the hypothesis is accepted when it is false.

The testing of the hypothesis is in two parts: if all the readings come from the same population, then there will be unique values for variance and mean. The possible variation of the ratio of the sample variances is first calculated. By eqn. 6.11.

$$\text{Prob}\,[s_1^2/s_2^2 > F_{n_1;n_2;\alpha}] = \alpha \qquad (6.12)$$

As $F > 0$, s_1 is always taken as the larger. Provided the ratio satisfies this criterion, the hypothesis of a common variance is acceptable at a level of significance of α. Once this is accepted a more accurate assessment of the variance can be made using both samples.

$$s = \{[(n_1 - 1)s_1^2 + (n_2 - 1)s_2^2]/(n_1 + n_2 - 2)\}^{1/2} \qquad (6.13)$$

one degree of freedom having been used to calculate the mean value of each sample. The variance of the mean values is

$$s_1^2/n_1 + s_2^2/n_2$$

and if these have a common sample variance s, the variance of the means becomes

$$s^2(1/n_1 + 1/n_2)$$

The distribution for mean values with an estimated variance is the Student t distribution of Section 2.8. Thus

$$\text{Prob}\,\{-s[(1/n_1) + (1/n_2)]^{1/2} t_{n_1 + n_2 - 2;\alpha/2} < \bar{x}_1 - \bar{x}_2$$
$$< s[(1/n_1) + (1/n_2)]^{1/2} t_{n_1 + n_2 - 2;\alpha/2}\} = \alpha \qquad (6.14)$$

and if the value of $\bar{x}_1 - \bar{x}_2$ lies between these limits, the null hypothesis can be accepted with a level of significance of α.

A slightly different hypothesis from the null hypothesis can be postulated. This states that the mean of the first sample is greater than or equal to the mean of the second. This hypothesis only requires one-sided testing, and the only difference is that the value of t used at a level of significance α is $t_{n_1 + n_2 - 2;\alpha}$ and *not* $t_{n_1 + n_2 - 2;\alpha/2}$, and only the positive limit is used.

When the variances of two populations are different but it is still required to postulate whether the means are the same, an approximate test can be performed using the following equation in place of eqn. (6.14):

$$\text{Prob}|-[(s_1^2/n_1) + (s_2^2/n_2)]^{1/2}t_{f;\alpha/2} < \bar{x}_1 - \bar{x}_2$$
$$< [(s_1^2/n_1) + (s_2^2/n_2)]^{1/2}t_{f;\alpha/2}| = \alpha \qquad (6.15)$$

where

$$f = \frac{[(s_1^2/n_1) + (s_2^2/n_2)]^2}{(s_1^2/n_1)/(n_1 + 1) + (s_2^2/n_2)^2/(n_2 + 1)} - 2$$

Interpolation is required in the use of tables.

6.4. CHI-SQUARE GOODNESS OF FIT TEST

The problem exists, whether it is in the context of the last section or not, of determining whether or not the points from an experimentally determined probability density function compare with a standard distribution. In 1900 Karl Pearson presented his 'Goodness of fit' criteria. He introduced a new variable D, where

$$D^2 = \sum_{i=1}^{N} (o_i - e_i)^2/e_i \qquad (6.16)$$

where o_i is the observed ith value, e_i the expected ith value and N the number of observations. Pearson postulated that the variable D^2 had a χ_{N-1}^2 distribution with $N - 1$ degrees of freedom (the loss of one degree of freedom is due to the fact that, having postulated the contents of the first $N - 1$ cells, the contents of the last cell are known). The author knows of no rigorous proof of this, but Meyer [34] shows that it approaches the chi-square distribution for large values of N.

The hypothesis that the fit is good is rejected if D^2, given by eqn. (6.16), is greater than a control value. With a thought for the type-1 error in the last paragraph when the hypothesis was erroneously rejected in 100α percent of the cases for which it was true, the same approach is used here.

The hypothesis of an acceptable fit is rejected if

$$D^2 > \chi_{N-1;\alpha}^2 \qquad (6.17)$$

where

$$\text{Prob}\,[\chi_N^2 > \chi_{N;\alpha}^2] = \alpha$$

and α is called the level of significance.

To carry out the estimation, the range of values possible is divided into cells or class intervals; in one case the intervals are of equal size and in the other they contain the same number of readings. The author much prefers the first and this is the one outlined here; the approach to the second should be obvious for anyone preferring that method.

The N readings of variable x are counted into K cells or class intervals (there should be about two and a half cells or class intervals for each standard deviation of the data) in an identical fashion to that described in Section 1.6. If x_i is the value of x at the top of the ith cell, then the number of readings which the standard distribution would expect there to be in the ith cell is given by

$$e_i = N \int_{x_{i-1}}^{x_i} p(x)\,\mathrm{d}x \qquad (6.18)$$

The counted number in the ith cell is o_i, so that the variable D^2 can be computed from eqn. (6.16). This value is compared with $\chi^2_{N-1;\alpha}$, where α can be as small as 0·05, and if $D^2 > \chi^2_{N-1;\alpha}$ the hypothesis that the data fit the standard curve is rejected at a level of significance of α.

Sometimes the value for α for which α is given by

$$D^2 = \chi^2_{N-1;\alpha} \qquad (6.19)$$

is determined and the fit is described as marginal at a level of significance of α. This allows the reader to make his own subjective assessment.

6.5. LINEAR CORRELATION OF TWO VARIABLES

In much of the work covered in Volume 1 two variables are related, and it is required to write

$$y = f(x)$$

When $f(x)$ is an involved function, it is sometimes possible to transform the variable x into another (t) such that there is a linear relationship between y and t, i.e.

$$y = a + bt$$

In this case when N pairs of values of x and y are measured they can be transformed into N pairs of values of y and t. The covariance coefficient function from eqn. (1.23) using r and s in preference to c and σ, because the values are determined from a sample only and are estimates, can be calculated as

$$r_{yt} = \overline{(y - \bar{y})(t - \bar{t})}/s_y s_t$$

When the data are obtained digitally, this becomes

$$r_{yt} = \left[\sum_{i=1}^{N}(y_i - \bar{y})(t_1 - \bar{t})\right]\left\{\left[\sum_{i=1}^{N}(y_i - \bar{y})^2\right]\left[\sum_{i=1}^{N}(t_1 - \bar{t})^2\right]\right\}^{-1/2}$$

$$= \left[\sum_{i=1}^{N}y_i t_i - N\bar{y}\bar{t}\right]\left\{\left[\sum_{i=1}^{N}y_i^2 - N\bar{y}^2\right]\left[\sum_{i=1}^{N}t_i^2 - N\bar{y}^2\right]\right\}^{-1/2} \quad (6.20)$$

In this context r_{yt} is sometimes called a 'correlation coefficient' and its value varies from $+1$ (perfect correlation) through 0 (zero correlation) to -1 (perfect antiphase correlation).

K. A. Brownlee suggests that a new variable, defined as

$$2\omega = \ln\left[(1 + r_{yt})/(1 - r_{yt})\right] \quad (6.21)$$

has a Gaussian distribution with a variance of

$$\sigma_\omega^2 = 1/(N - 3) \quad (6.22)$$

By a procedure similar to that in Section 6.2.1, it follows that the true value of ω (μ_ω) lies between the limits

$$\omega - z_{\alpha/2}/(N - 3)^{1/2} \leq \mu_\omega < \omega + z_{\alpha/2}/(N - 3)^{1/2} \quad (6.23)$$

with a confidence coefficient of $(1 - \alpha)$ where

$$\text{Prob}\,[z < z_\alpha] = \alpha \quad .$$

for a Gaussian distribution.

6.6.   LINEAR REGRESSION

It is often required to fit a straight line to experimental points defined as

$$y = a + bt \quad (6.24)$$

The usual method is called the 'method of least squares'. One variable is defined as independent and the other as dependent. With the relationship in the form of eqn. (6.24) t would be defined as independent and y as dependent. The method calculates the difference between the actual reading of y for a given value of t and that estimated by eqn. (6.19). Values of a and b are determined such that the sum of the squares of the differences for all pairs of measured points is a minimum.

Thus the difference term D is defined as

$$D = \sum_{i=1}^{N} (y_i - a - bt_i)^2$$

and for minimum difference

$$dD/da = dD/db = 0$$

This gives values of a and b

$$b = \left(\sum_{i=1}^{N} x_i y_i - N\bar{x}\bar{y} \right) \Big/ \left(\sum_{i=1}^{N} x_i^2 - N\bar{x}^2 \right) \tag{6.25}$$

and

$$a = \bar{y} - b\bar{x} \tag{6.26}$$

The differences between the measured y and that determined by eqn. (6.24) are random, and as the variance of the differences

$$s_{\Delta y}^2 = D/(N - 2) \tag{6.27}$$

is estimated, Section 6.2.3 would suggest that the Student t distribution applies. This means that a common confidence interval can be specified at all values of x:

$$\text{Prob}\,[y_{\text{line}} - st_{N-2;\alpha/2}(1/\sqrt{N}) \le y_{\text{true}} < y_{\text{line}} + st_{N-2;\alpha/2}(1/\sqrt{N})] = (1 - \alpha) \tag{6.28}$$

The term $(N - 2)$ in eqns. (6.27) and (6.28) signifies the loss of two degrees of freedom due to the calculation of a and b.

K. A. Brownlee considered that a band of constant width over the whole range of values of x was unrealistic, and that the band ought to be wider at its extremities. He therefore suggested that the term $[1/\sqrt{N}]$ in eqn. (6.28) be replaced by

$$\left\{ (1/N) + (x_0 - \bar{x})^2 \Big/ \left[\sum_{i=1}^{N} (x_i - \bar{x})^2 \right] \right\}^{1/2} \tag{6.29}$$

where the confidence interval from the modified eqn. (6.28) is applied, where x has the value x_0.

This approaches somewhat the idea of variable-width confidence bands already used in Section 5.9, but in that case the number of readings varied along the 'line' so that a more definite relationship could be specified.

6.7. BEST LINEAR UNBIASED ESTIMATOR (BLUE) METHOD

For reasons given by Mann [32], the least squares method gives a biased (in the statistical sense) estimate for the mode and dispersion for the Fisher–Tippett type-I extreme value distribution. A method to give the coefficients of a *best* unbiased straight line through the points is contained in Ref. 28. The method presents values for coefficients such that the mode U and dispersion α can be calculated from eqns. (6.30) and (6.31):

$$U = \sum_{M=1}^{N} A_M X_M \tag{6.30}$$

and

$$1/\alpha = \sum_{M=1}^{N} B_M X_M \tag{6.31}$$

where X_M are the ranked values described in Section 5.5 and defined by eqn. (5.18).

The difficulty with the method is one of organisation, because a different set of coefficients must be used depending upon the number of extreme values available (N). Leiblein [28] tabulates the coefficients (270 in all) for numbers of extreme values from 2 to 16.

Two further methods for calculating *very good* linear unbiased estimators of the mode and dispersion for larger samples than 16 are also given in Ref. 28. For very large ($N > 50$) samples the method consists of extracting four selected values and evaluating the mode and dispersion using eqns. (6.30) and (6.31) with four new coefficients (A_i^* and B_i^*). The method for selecting the appropriate values is detailed. Thus

$$U = \sum_{i=1}^{4} A_i^* X_{M_i} \tag{6.32}$$

and

$$\alpha = \sum_{i=1}^{4} B_i^* X_{M_i} \tag{6.33}$$

where $i = 1, 2, 3, 4$ correspond to specific readings given by

$$M_i = \lambda_i N \tag{6.34}$$

and values for λ_i are given.

For intermediate numbers of samples ($16 < N < 50$) another method is given which consists of using the coefficient for the best estimator for a sample of 10 values (any large number (J) can be chosen, but 10 is recommended), and evaluating good estimators for the N coefficients required using the expression

$$A'_M = \sum_{t=1}^{J} [A_t(t/M)p(N, J, M, |t)] \tag{6.35}$$

and

$$B'_M = \sum_{t=1}^{J} [B_t(t/M)p(N, J, M, t)] \tag{6.36}$$

where A_t and B_t are the BLUE coefficients for a sample of size J and $p(N, J, M, t)$ is the hypergeometric probability distribution function which is given by

$p(N, J, M, t)$

$$= \frac{M!}{(M-t)!} \frac{J!}{(J-t)!\,t!} \frac{1}{t!} \frac{(N-M)!}{N!} \frac{(N-J)!}{(N-M-J+t)!} \tag{6.37}$$

The mode and dispersion are given by eqns. (6.30) and (6.31), with coefficients A'_M and B'_M replacing the BLUE values A_M and B_M.

For all these estimators to be unbiased

$$\sum_{M=1}^{N} A_M = 1$$

and

$$\sum_{M=1}^{N} B_M = 0$$

When tabular values are used for $N < 16$ and $N > 50$ these conditions are met; it is worth checking that the values devised by the method for the intermediate values also satisfy these conditions, and minor alterations should be made in rounding procedures to ensure they are satisfied at whatever degree of accuracy is being used.

7

Meteorology: Introduction to Weather Systems

The job of the wind engineer is to analyse the wind loading upon a building or its wind and pollution environment. To carry out this work effectively, data about the wind are required. The question posed in this Chapter is, 'Need anything be known about meteorology, or are sufficient data generally available in the correct format?'

The following is a list of requirements which would satisfy all the needs of Volume 1:

(i)   An hourly average windspeed which has a quoted probability of being exceeded in any one year, measured at a height of 10 m above open, flat, level ground in the vicinity of the building. This is called the 'meteorological standard windspeed' in these volumes.

(ii)   The variation of this windspeed around the world.

(iii)   The variation of this windspeed with height over different kinds of terrain.

(iv)   The variation of turbulence intensity with height in the same conditions.

(v)   The spectrum of turbulence at a number of heights in the same conditions.

(vi)   Certain correlations of windspeed at two points in space and other complex statistical descriptions of wind.

(vii)   Frequency of simultaneous windspeed and wind direction at sites around the world.

As it is unusual to find a meteorological station at many building sites, by 'site' is implied the nearest meteorological station, provided it is reasonably close to the site and in a terrain where climatic conditions are similar.

Consider a programme of measurement which would provide these data. The hourly average windspeed can be measured by an anemometer and wind vane placed on the top of a mast at a site. Frequency of windspeed and direction can be obtained from the results, assuming they are of sufficient duration (about 20 years). The limitation to this work is the number of sites covered, which is financial, and not the complexity of measurement.

The variation of mean windspeed and turbulence intensity with height can be measured in a research experiment by mounting a series of anemometers at a number of heights up several masts which are located in a variety of environments, and recording the windspeeds during the passage of many storms.

The value of windspeed which has the required probability of being exceeded in any year can be derived from the frequency of windspeed data by extreme value analysis, which can then be corrected for 10 m height and 'open, flat, level country' ground roughness conditions by the results of the research experiments. By these means the value of the 'meteorological standard windspeed' can be derived for the site and repetition at many sites would give worldwide coverage.

By plotting the values of the meteorological standard windspeed for all the sites on a map and drawing isotachs, it is possible both to smooth the values and to find the effect of the local topography of the site. This correction can be applied to the frequency of windspeed and direction data to remove shelter or exposure effects of the local topography of the anemometer station.

The basic results from the research experiments can be further examined by statistical methods to obtain spectra of windspeed and turbulence and, by the use of several towers, closely spaced, to obtain two-point data.

This procedure is quite practicable and has now been attempted with limited success. When the results of the research experiments were studied, it was found that the variations with height from the series of measurements collapsed into unique curves for these occasions when the mean windspeed was high, but, as the lower limit for the collapse of curves was a mean windspeed of $10\,\mathrm{m\,s}^{-1}$, the derivation of the meteorological standard windspeed was successful. For the lower windspeeds, however, a large number of variations was obtained and this was found to be due to variations of stability within the atmosphere. Not only does the atmosphere have a range of stability values over the whole layer; it also has thin strata within the atmosphere in which the stability (see Section 8.2 for the relationship between stability and temperature gradient) is radically different from the rest of the atmosphere. These combinations constitute an almost infinite variety of possible conditions and it would be reasonable to expect that each was related to a different variation of windspeed parameter with height.

It would appear that the experimentalist could derive the required data about high windspeeds without assistance from a meteorologist. However, complications now arise. The techniques so far described will work provided the weather system is so large that it spans several meteorological stations as it traverses the country, and provided weather systems of the type to give the design windspeeds occur reasonably frequently (many times a year). If the weather system is so small that it could pass between stations without its major effects being recorded, or if it occurred only once in every few years, then the above technique would be inadequate. The first need for a meteorologist in the context of buildings in the wind is to explain the size and frequency of weather systems and to help to interpret the results which an experimentalist can measure.

The other two topics which require discussion are concerned with the treatment of the atmospheric boundary layer as a classical boundary layer; these are fetch and equilibrium over the whole height. These require comment by meteorologists.

Because of this fact it is necessary to introduce a little elementary meteorology. The next few sections present those topics which are pertinent to the discussion of these points.

7.1. THE SOLAR DRIVING FORCE

Winds are basically created by the differential heating of the atmosphere by the sun. As the sun's rays approach the earth most of the solar energy, at wavelengths at which the air can absorb the energy, is absorbed by the air in the mesosphere, the upper regions of the atmosphere where the assumption that air is a continuum first becomes tenable, which is far too high to be of interest to this work. Thereafter the solar rays have no energy of a wavelength which can be absorbed directly by the air. The sun's rays therefore pass through the air and fall on the ground (or cloud) and are absorbed. In the case of the ground, some of the energy is retransmitted at different wavelengths which can be absorbed by the air. For this reason, even though the energy to heat the atmosphere is supplied by the sun, the air temperature at the surface is highest, decreasing with height for the first 10 km of the atmosphere: the earth's surface can therefore be considered as the effective source of heat for the air and the importance of the texture of the earth's surface becomes evident.

Because for a given land area the projected area normal to the sun's rays (adjusted to a minor extent by the inclination of the axis about which the earth spins) is much greater at the Equator than at the Poles, the equatorial regions become hotter than the polar ones. A temperature gradient and its associated density and pressure gradients would create a circulation on a completely homogeneous earth, as shown in Fig. 7.1.

The rotation of a homogeneous earth and the associated surface friction cause this single circulation to break up into three separate circulations in

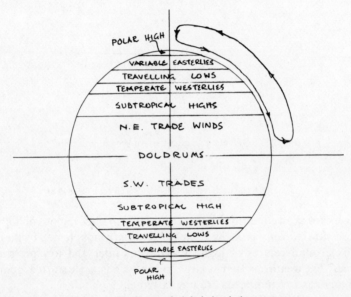

Fig. 7.1. Fundamental global circulation pattern.

each of the Northern and Southern Hemispheres. The resultant pattern is shown in Fig. 7.2, on which the names of the regions have been added. It is interesting to note the nautical flavour of these names, conceived by the sailors of the 19th century but still in use today.

The earth's surface, however, is not homogeneous; it contains large masses of land and sea. Their presence causes these three belts in each hemisphere to develop a longitudinal rearrangement of pressure, called 'cells', incidentally producing corridors in the prevailing winds. The inclination of the earth's rotation axis to the ecliptic causes a seasonal change in these cells—in winter there is the Icelandic low and the Siberian high which covers most of Europe and much of Asia, and in summer there is a sub-tropical high over the Azores which, to some extent, fills the Icelandic low.

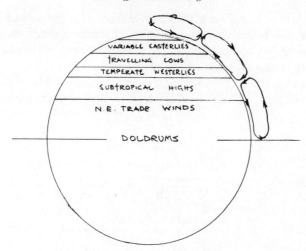

Fig. 7.2. Global circulation pattern broken into cells.

7.2. Monsoons and Hurricanes (Typhoons)

Two types of wind condition are directly related to these regions of high and low pressure. A *monsoon* is the name given to the winds created by the cells, usually around centres of high pressure in winter and low pressure in summer. The weather system is large and the winds, once started, continue for many days. Windspeeds are not extremely high.

The second form of storm driven directly by the world circulation system is the *hurricane*. Warm moist air is carried to high altitude by the vertical velocities of the cell close to the Equator at latitudes between 5° and 20°. When conditions are suitable, the warm moist air forms tall convective clouds in which condensation occurs and releases latent heat in immense quantities because of the size of the hurricane (up to 1000 km in diameter). The energy drives the wind in a rotary motion in the inner region, which becomes a vortex, causing air to be sucked inwards along the ground into the core up through the vortex, to be rejected radially at high level (10 km to 17 km altitude). Conditions in the very centre of the vortex are calm, as in any vortex (compare the Rankine Vortex) and this region is called the 'eye of the hurricane'.

The hurricane contains more energy than any other storm process and can last for considerable periods (many days) because it is continually generating energy from the latent heat of condensation of new water vapour as more and more warm moist air is drawn into the vortex as the hurricane travels over the land or sea. The condensation means that hurricanes are usually associated with very heavy rain. Surface windspeeds in excess of $75\,\mathrm{m\,s^{-1}}$ (about 150 mph) can be encountered in hurricanes.

7.3. TEMPERATE WEATHER SYSTEMS

No other weather system is related directly to the world circulation pattern; all others are consequences of events produced by it. The most important result of these large high- and low-pressure regions is that large masses of air tend to move, and tend to take with them evidence of their origins so they are called arctic, polar or tropical. As these air masses travel, their water content depends upon their track and those having a *maritime* track will tend to become saturated, especially in the lower layers. On the other hand, those having a *continental* track will retain a dewpoint similar to their original value, because there has been little water to acquire. Polar air flowing to lower latitudes is warmed from below and becomes unstable (see Section 8.2); tropical air flowing to higher latitudes is cooled from below and becomes stable. Slow vertical air movements are produced by divergence near the ground (for example, near developing anticyclones) when air sinks slowly and by convergence near the ground (for example, near developing depressions) when the air rises slowly.

When two air masses meet, the line of discontinuity is called a 'front' (originally named by V. Bjerkness in 1917); it is called a warm front when warm air moves into cold air and usually rides up over the cold air at a shallow angle, and a cold front when cold air moves into warm air and causes it to rise abruptly. An 'occlusion' or occluded front is when a cold front has caught up with a warm front and has pushed all the warm air up and continuous cold air exists at ground level.

In temperate zones therefore, the winds are created by the movement of air masses which provide long-term (up to 4 days) prevailing wind conditions over large areas; the presence of mountain ranges affects these conditions locally. At fronts rapid changes of conditions can occur and fast vertical movements of air are possible. This can lead to temperate or extratropical cyclones, whose most widely known and active manifestation is a *thunderstorm*.

The overall description of a thunderstorm is very similar to that of a hurricane, with two major differences. Firstly, it is small and is usually related to and caused by a front; secondly, the upflows and downflows are reversed. Professor Ludlum's illustration [30] of a thunderstorm is reproduced in Fig. 7.3; the cold air has pushed the warm moist air upwards, condensation has taken place and has released energy and the downflow of air accompanies the downward path of the rain. Some of the rain evaporates, cooling the air which flows outward from the centre along the ground. The scale (about 10 km in diameter) and the vertical velocities are

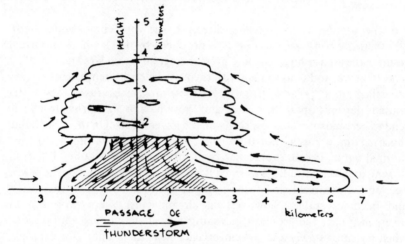

Fig. 7.3. Sketch of thunderstorm (after a sketch by Professor Ludlum, 1956).

much smaller than in a hurricane and the windspeeds are much lower, both because of the energy available and because of the reversed radial direction of motion. The lifetime of the thunderstorm (the order of one hour) is much shorter than that of a hurricane because the energy within it is limited.

However, within a severe thunderstorm it is possible for *tornadoes* to develop. These are small vortices which form within the thunderstorm and, by application of the principle of conservation of momentum, tend to reduce their diameter to about 300 m and increase their tangential velocity to above $100 \, \mathrm{m \, s^{-1}}$. One of the standard features of vortices is the low pressure in the centre or core, which is related to the tangential velocity and the radius. As a consequence of the combination of high windspeeds and small radius in a tornado, this pressure reduction in the core can be considerable (the order of $10^4 \, \mathrm{N \, m^{-2}}$). This very low pressure causes objects in the path of the tornado to be lifted, so that tornadoes are often filled with water, sand, dust or debris and are thereby made visible. The lifetime of a tornado is short (usually of the order of minutes to tens of

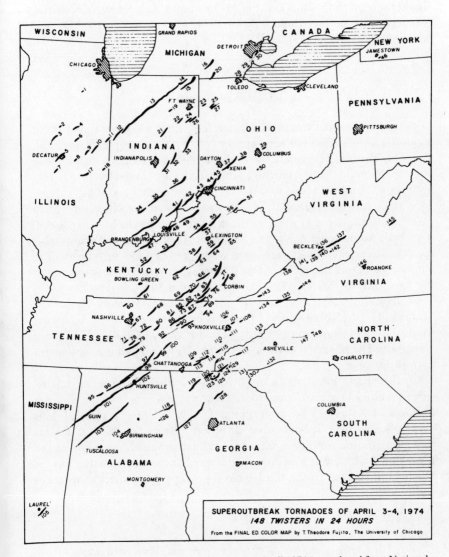

Fig. 7.4. Location of tornadoes in the USA on 3–4 April 1974 (reproduced from National Academy of Sciences [35]).

minutes), but it is possible for many tornadoes to develop and die within a single thunderstorm situation. Figure 7.4 shows such a cluster occurring over the USA on the 3 and 4 April 1974, as reported by the National Academy of Sciences [35].

7.4. LOCAL WINDS

Local conditions can create or affect winds; some are general and occur around the world and others are specific to a geographical location. Probably the best known are the onshore/offshore breezes which blow in coastal regions in the daytime/night-time. These are caused by the different abilities of land and sea to absorb and retransmit the solar energy. Mountain ranges in general, by creating vertical velocities, are often associated with rain and wind, as the last two paragraphs have explained. Katabatic winds in the Arctic and Antarctic are of widespread occurrence; the winds are generally of high mean windspeed and low turbulence. The windiest place on earth is Port Martin, where the average hourly windspeed for the month of March 1952 was Beaufort force 11 [29]!

In several specific geographical locations, named winds blow. The Mistral down the Rhône valley in France is similar in origin to the katabatic winds but the temperatures, and therefore the windspeeds, are more temperate. The Bora in the Adriatic is of similar origin, but the subsequent path is different.

In other special locations the origins of the wind are conventional, but the subsequent passage introduces special features: for example, the winds in Sheffield, UK. Here the determining feature is three ranges of hills perpendicular to a specific wind direction. When the wind is in this direction, the three ranges appear as an undulating surface across which the wind flows, accelerating with each dip until disgorged into the city of Sheffield at the end of the third cycle [1]. Many other specific instances could be cited.

7.5. QUESTIONS TO BE ANSWERED BY THE METEOROLOGIST

The only small weather systems which could miss the measuring stations are tornadoes, and wind data for areas where these occur (and the Meteorologist is required to say where that is) need special treatment.

When annual maxima are used in the extreme value analysis to calculate the meteorological standard windspeed for areas where tornadoes occur, it is usual for the highest winds in some years to be of tornado origin and in other years, in which the tornadoes have missed the station, to be of extratropical cyclonic origin. If all the annual maxima windspeeds were plotted against the reduced variate on a single extreme value curve and a best-fit line drawn through them all and then extrapolated to a design condition, the line would be misleading. This is because the measurements come from a mixed population—tornadoes and extratropical storms. The correct procedure would be to separate the two and develop separate probability density functions for the windspeeds in tornadoes and in extratropical storms, and to treat the problem as one associated with mixed populations (Section 5.11). A further complication must be introduced in that the probability density function for the tornado windspeed is a joint probability (Section 2.15) of windspeed in the tornado and its adjustment because of the distance of the site from the tornado core.

Meteorologists become essential in conditions in which the value of the meteorological standard windspeed is less than $10 \, \mathrm{m \, s^{-1}}$, because of the multitude of different conditions which can prevail. This has already been explained in the introduction to this chapter.

To summarise the conclusions to date: experimental results can be obtained and applied generally for high windspeeds in regions of the world where hurricanes and tornadoes do not occur. Where meteorologists say these storms can occur, a mixed population approach should be made, but to date the experimental data on windspeeds within these storms and their frequency and track are scanty and efforts are required to obtain more complete coverage of data. In problems in which low windspeeds provide the design condition, the Meteorologist should be consulted to find whether any local condition prevails; if not, the 'frequency of windspeed and direction' tables provide adequate information and it is usual to assume that the variation of wind parameters with height is the same as for high winds. This is almost certainly wrong, but the possible variations are legion and cannot be quantified. Of particular importance are stable atmospheres, or strata within the atmosphere, because these extract energy from the wind (see Section 8.2) which reduces both mean windspeeds and turbulence and thereby reduce dilution from a plume into the atmosphere.

Theorists and experimentalists such as Deaves and Harris or ESDU can provide data, but the meteorologist will always be needed to say when the various parts of the data can be used, and to comment upon low-windspeed conditions.

7.6. EQUILIBRIUM AND FETCH

These two questions remain. When wind blows over a homogeneous rough surface for a very considerable distance, the boundary layer is in equilibrium at all heights and would continue so for the continuation of the surface. When the surface changes from one homogeneous state to another such state of different surface roughness, the consequences of the change are transmitted to the air at heights above the surface by viscous and eddy forces, the height of the discontinuity increasing with distance downwind of the change. In practice, the roughness of the earth's surface is continually changing, so that the layer is never in equilibrium; in consequence all measured profiles are compromises and all equations representing functions have been smoothed. 'Fetch' is the name given to the distance upwind of the site at which the last major change of surface roughness took place.

Throughout this section it has been assumed that the atmospheric boundary layer was similar to a classical boundary layer in which the wind has blown for a considerable distance over a surface, albeit of changing roughness. The above description of thunderstorms in which much air travels downwards in the centre and outwards over the ground cannot truly be of this nature within the thunderstorm. Fortunately, the duration of the energetic part of a thunderstorm will usually prevent this storm from creating the maximum hourly average windspeed. It is therefore reasonable to assume that the very occasional high windspeeds are associated with classical boundary layer type flow. The vertical variation of gust speeds (windspeeds averaged over 3 s) is found experimentally to be different; this could be either because they are caused by thunderstorms or because they require to be satisfied by the requirements of conservation of mass, which would suggest less variation with height for gust speeds than for hourly average windspeeds.

8

Meteorology: Introduction to Fluid Mechanics

Chapter 7 attempted to outline the physical processes by which wind is created, and concluded in Section 7.6 that there are great difficulties and many assumptions made in presenting numerical values of the parameters describing the wind. However the wind obeys the laws of fluid mechanics. This chapter outlines these laws and attempts to explain how a logical framework, within which the performance of buildings in the wind can be examined, can be derived.

8.1. Generation of Wind in Temperate Zones

Wind in the first instance is caused by the differential heating of the air. All gases have three properties—pressure (p), temperature (T) and density (ρ), —related by the equation of state

$$p = \rho RT \tag{8.1}$$

where R is the gas constant for air. When any one parameter changes, such as temperature due to heating by the sun, changes are produced in the other two. If all the change took place in the density, the heated volume would expand displacing the air above and to all sides of it; if all the change took place in the pressure, regions of higher pressure than their surroundings would be formed and as these pressure differences cannot be sustained, air would move to cancel the pressure differences. In practice, both pressure and density change, but as the latter is a phenomenon which works on a shorter time scale it tends to predominate.

At first glance the wind ought to move from regions of high pressure to those at a lower pressure. The movement starts in this way, but the earth's rotation plays a part. For air to move in a curved path there must be a

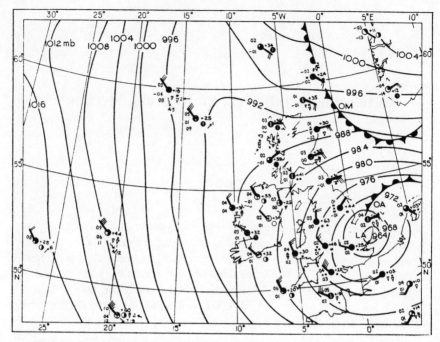

Fig. 8.1. Superposition of windspeed and direction arrows on map showing isobars.

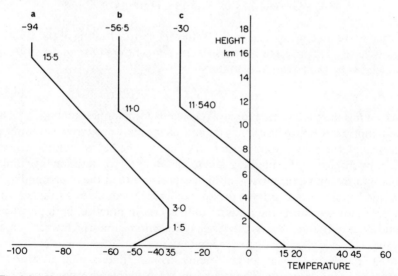

Fig. 8.2. Variation of air temperature with height in 'standard' atmospheres. (a) Arctic minimum, (b) ISA, (c) tropical maximum.

higher pressure on the outside of the path than on the inside. This is analogous to the child's conker on the end of a piece of string; a tension in the string is required to maintain the conker in its curved path. Thus the wind direction is fairly closely aligned to the isobars due to rotation of the earth and its atmosphere (see Fig. 8.1).

For reasons explained in Section 7.1, the earth can be considered to be the effective source of heat for the air, and the variation of air temperature with height is shown in Fig. 8.2. This region of the atmosphere in which the temperature varies with height is called the troposphere, terminated at the top by the tropopause. This explains the importance of the texture of the earth's surface at the location in question, and especially how local wind can be changed when large areas of concrete or other white substance are laid over farmland.

This then is a very simplified explanation of the mechanism for the creation of wind.

8.2. STATIC STABILITY OF THE ATMOSPHERE

A parcel of air is in equilibrium at height h_1 (see Fig. 8.3) where its density is ρ_1 and pressure p_1. Suppose it is lifted quickly to a greater height h_2 and that no heat is added to the air; then the system is called stable if it is more dense than the surrounding air and consequently descends to its original height.

The change of pressure with height in the static case is expressed by the

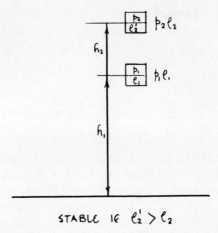

Fig. 8.3. Sketch explaining static stability of the atmosphere.

hydrostatic equation, which states that the atmospheric pressure on a unit horizontal area is the result of the weight of all the air above. Thus

$$p = p_0 + \rho g h \tag{8.2}$$

Measurements show that temperature varies in a linear fashion up to the tropopause at about 10 km, so for this region

$$T = T_0 - \lambda h \tag{8.3}$$

where λ is called the lapse rate.

Differentiating eqn. (8.2) and eliminating the density by eqn. (8.1) gives

$$\partial p/\partial h = -\rho g = -pg/RT$$

$$\frac{\partial p}{p} = \frac{-g\partial h}{R(T_0 - \lambda h)} = \frac{g}{\lambda R}\frac{\partial(T_0 - \lambda h)}{(T_0 - \lambda h)}$$

$$p/p_0 = [(T_0 - \lambda h)/T_0]^{g/\lambda R} \tag{8.4}$$

$$p = p_0[1 - \lambda h/T_0]^{g/\lambda R}$$

$$T = T_0[1 - \lambda h/T_0]$$

so that

$$\rho = \rho_0[1 - \lambda h/T_0]^{(g/\lambda R)-1}$$

When the parcel of air was lifted with no heat addition the process would have been adiabatic, so that

$$p/\rho^\gamma = \text{constant} \tag{8.5}$$

This equation can be satisfied with the form of solution for eqn. (8.4), because the form of eqn. (8.5) can be produced by eqn. (8.4):

$$p/\rho^\gamma = p_0/\rho_0^\gamma[1 - \lambda h/T_D]^{(g/\lambda R)-(\gamma g/\lambda R)+\gamma}$$

which is the same as eqn. (8.5) if

$$g/\lambda R - \gamma g/\lambda R + \gamma = 0$$

or

$$\lambda = (g/R)[(\gamma - 1)/\gamma] \tag{8.6}$$

λ, defined by eqn. (8.6), is called the adiabatic lapse rate. This is an important value because it forms the boundary between an unstable (superadiabatic) and a stable (subadiabatic) atmosphere. In the unstable atmosphere, when a parcel of air is displaced from its equilibrium height to another height, it continues to move away from its original equilibrium position: hence the term 'unstable'. A further implication is that in the unstable condition work is done by the buoyancy forces on the wind, causing energy to be fed into the wind and increasing the windspeed and the turbulence velocities to values greater than those expected in a neutral atmosphere.

Conversely, in a stable atmosphere the lapse rate is greater than that for the neutral atmosphere and when this condition applies a parcel of air moved away from its equilibrium position will tend to return to it. This implies that work is done against the buoyancy forces by the flow and energy is extracted from the wind, so that both the mean windspeed and the turbulence velocities are reduced compared to neutral conditions and may indeed vanish altogether. This type of atmosphere, or part of the atmosphere where these conditions prevail, is of special importance in the study of effluent plumes and will be considered separately in the next section.

8.3. INVERSIONS

Inversions are layers of the atmosphere which have great static stability. Their importance lies, as far as wind effects on buildings is concerned, in the behaviour of effluent plumes. When a city lies in a hollow conditions can persist which maintain an inversion at a small height above the rim of the surrounding landscape. This can become dramatically obvious to an observer at some location near the rim because the smoke, steam, etc., from the city rises gently until it reaches this level and then, finding itself unable to penetrate the layer, tends to spread out along its underside, creating a layer of pollution which can spread over the whole city.

Thin stable layers somewhat higher from the ground can produce turbulence through a mechanism known as the Kelvin–Helmholst instability. The mechanism does require some wave motion to be present, so this occurrence happens most often downwind of mountain ranges and is called clear air turbulence (CAT) because it appears in the absence of any visible turbulence-making phenomena. Mountain ranges are not essential for the generation of CAT, but are often associated with it.

8.4. THE ATMOSPHERIC BOUNDARY LAYER

There are two possible types of fluid flow—laminar and turbulent. Laminar flow represents the condition when the fluid can be considered as a series of laminae sliding one over the other. There is no requirement for the laminae to travel at the same speed; when different, there is a 'frictional' force between them. Turbulent flow occurs when the flow is not laminar and represents the case when particles of the fluid at a given instant flow in many directions with many speeds: values of windspeed and direction at any location are average values only.

A fluid has a property called 'viscosity', which is an ability to resist deformation and is similar to the property of a sheet of metal to resist shear forces. In the latter case the shear stress τ is proportional to the shear deformation dx/dy and the constant of proportionality is called the shear modulus G:

$$\tau = G\,dx/dy$$

For the fluid the term 'shear stress' is used, which is proportional to the rate of slide (du/dz). The constant of proportionality is called the 'coefficient of viscosity'

$$\tau = \mu\,du/dz \tag{8.7}$$

In laminar flow pressure and shear stresses are the only ones which occur. In turbulent flow there is another stress due to the random movements of the particles of fluid, which, because it is similar to the shear stress, is called a Reynolds stress and is written

$$\tau_{uw} = \overline{\rho u(t)w(t)} \tag{8.8}$$

where $u(t)$ and $w(t)$ are the fluctuating components of velocity in the two dimensions concerned $((1/T)\int_0^T u(t)\,dt = 0$ by definition). There are three Reynolds stresses combining the components of windspeed in the three mutually perpendicular directions.

Newton's second law of motion can be applied to a parcel of air in motion. This states that, when a force is applied to a mass of air, it produces a rate of change of momentum in the direction of the applied force. Provided the mass of the parcel does not change with time, it is simpler to consider that the force produces an acceleration. When applied to an element of air the equations which ensue are usually called the Navier–Stokes equations of motion, and no general closed-form solution for these equations has been produced.

Prandtl studied practical examples of the flow of air over a surface as well as these equations and found that the shear stresses were only comparable in magnitude to the pressure stresses in a thin layer of fluid close to the surface. Away from the surface the values of $\partial u/\partial z$ and $(\overline{u(t)w(t)})$ tended to become small. He then postulated a thin layer close to the surface in which shear forces were important, which he called the 'boundary layer'. Outside this thin layer the shear stresses could be ignored and only pressure forces applied—the flow in this region is called 'potential flow'.

This division of the flow field allowed Prandtl to make important simplifications to the equations: in the potential flow regions he ignored shear stresses entirely and produced simpler equations which could be solved. In the boundary layer region he studied the 'orders of magnitude' of the various terms in the Navier–Stokes equations and found that for a thin layer (z small compared with x) great simplifications could be produced. This division of the subject is now part of aerodynamics.

The wind over the earth, which was discussed in Section 8.1, is identical to the flow of air over a surface and will produce a thin boundary layer; this is called the atmospheric boundary layer. It varies in thickness according to the roughness of the surface. Values of thickness (called gradient height) are estimated to be between 500 m and 3 km; eqn. (8.14) gives an expression from which they can be calculated.

8.5. GRADIENT HEIGHT AND GRADIENT WINDSPEED

In the general boundary layer, conditions are governed by the velocity at the upper edge, usually called the free stream velocity, by the roughness at the surface, and its depth which is called the boundary layer thickness.

In the atmosphere the height of the layer is called the 'gradient height' and the windspeed at the upper edge the 'gradient windspeed'. The term 'gradient' in both these expresses the thought that conditions here are produced by pressure gradients alone.

The gradient windspeed is considered as the driving force for the wind and the impediment is the ground roughness. In some circumstances it is convenient to reduce both terms to comparable units, so a friction velocity U^* is defined such that the shear stress at the ground (τ_0) is related to the friction velocity by the equation

$$\tau_0 = \rho U^{*2} \qquad (8.9)$$

It is found that the frictional velocity is the correct scaling windspeed throughout the layer.

In his studies of turbulent boundary layers in the laboratory, Coles divided the layers into two parts—an inner part for which he specified a law of the wall and an outer part for which he postulated a law of the wake. The difference between these two parts is the scaling length used. Close to the wall the length is one associated with the surface roughness and in the upper part of the boundary layer it is one associated with the boundary layer thickness.

8.6. Surface Roughness Height z_0

Monin and Oberoff showed that, when the shear stress is constant, the variation of mean velocity with height in the atmosphere can be written in the form

$$V = (U^*/k)\ln(z/z_0) \qquad (8.10)$$

where z_0 is called the roughness height and k is Von Karman's constant and is equal to 0·4. In the original experimental work in which the rough surfaces were produced by sticking sand over the surface to produce a homogeneous or, to be more accurate, self-similar roughness, the roughness height was proportional to the grain size of the sand. In non-similar roughness, different sized elements adhere to the surface in a random pattern and the density of elements, as well as some measure of their various sizes, must be considered. The value of z_0 is no longer directly related to the size of the elements producing the roughness. For instance, for newly mown grass z_0 is about 6×10^{-3} m, which could be related to the thickness of the grass mat, but for the centre of a city its value is about 1·5 m, which could not.

The law of the wake for the outer region is a defect law, in that the decrease in velocity from that in the free stream is specified. It usually takes the form

$$(U_0 - U)/U^* = f_1(z/\delta)$$

where U_0 is the free stream velocity and δ the boundary layer thickness. In the atmospheric boundary layer context this becomes

$$(V_G - V)/U^* = f_1(z/H) \qquad (8.11)$$

where V_G is the gradient windspeed and H is the gradient height.

The form of expression which would approach eqns. (8.10) and (8.11) at either limit must be of the form

$$V = (U^*/k)[\ln(z/z_0) + f_2(z/H)] \qquad (8.12)$$

Substitution of eqn. (8.12) into eqn. (8.11) gives

$$V_G/U^* = (1/k)[\ln(z/z_0) + f_1(z/H) + f_2(z/H)]$$

but the value of V_G can be calculated directly from eqn. (8.12) with $z = H$ thus:

$$V_G/U^* = (1/k)[\ln{(H/z_0)} + f_2(1)] \tag{8.13}$$

By equating these expressions, it follows that the gradient height must be related to the friction velocity by an expression of the form

$$H = U^*/\beta f \tag{8.14}$$

where f is the Coriolis parameter and is given by

$$f = 2\omega \sin{\phi}$$

where $\omega \equiv$ angular rate of rotation of the earth $= 72.7 \times 10^{-6}\,\text{rad s}^{-1}$
$\phi \equiv$ local angle of latitude
β is a constant.

On substitution of eqn. (8.14) into eqn. (8.13),

$$V_G/U^* = (1/k)[\ln{(U^*/fz_0)} - \ln{(\beta)} + f_2(1)]$$

and by fitting measured profiles Deaves and Harris find that a best fit is obtained if $[f_2(1) - \ln{(\beta)}]$ equals unity together with a value of 6 for β, so that $f_2(1) = 1 + \ln{6} = 2.792$.

The general expression for the variation of mean windspeed through the atmosphere (eqn. (8.12)) is re-examined in the light of the experimentally determined constants β and $f_2(1)$. The function $f_2(z/H)$ is expanded as a polynomial with four terms and the coefficients a_1 to a_4 are determined theoretically to give

$$V = (U^*/k)[\ln{(z/z_0)} + 5.75(z/H) - 1.87(z/H)^2$$
$$- 1.33(z/H)^3 + 0.25(z/H)^4] \tag{8.15}$$

For the lower 200 m of the atmosphere, the contributions from the square, cube and fourth-order terms can be omitted to obtain the simpler expression

$$V = (U^*/k)[\ln{(z/z_0)} + 5.75(z/H)] \tag{8.16}$$

A criticism often made of this log law relationship is that it was derived for a region of constant shear stress ($z \le 30\,\text{m}$) and yet it is applied well beyond the height at which the shear stress ceases to be constant. This argument is erroneous, because the law of the wall (e.g. eqn. 8.10) applied to the constant shear stress region was one limiting condition for the matching eqn. (8.12), so that the final matching eqn. (8.15) is only required to conform to constant shear stress at its limit, which it does.

When H from eqn. (8.14) is substituted into eqn. (8.15) and z is equated to 10 m, a relationship between z_0 and U^* is obtained in terms of the mean windspeed at 10 m:

$$V_{10} = (U^*/k)\ln(10/z_0) + 5{\cdot}75(10\beta f/U^*)(U^*/k)$$
$$= (U^*/k)\ln(10/z_0) + 5{\cdot}75(10\beta f/k)$$

i.e.

$$U^* = k(V_{10} - 0{\cdot}1)/\ln(10/z_0) \tag{8.17}$$

for $53°$ latitude when $f = 1{\cdot}161 \times 10^{-4}$.

For most applications this can be simplified to

$$U^* = kV_{10}/\ln(10/z_0) \tag{8.18}$$

8.7. ZERO PLANE DISPLACEMENT

Consider a basic surface with small surface roughness. Counihan [7] describes an experiment in which the floor of his wind tunnel is covered with Lego baseboard. To increase the surface roughness, he adds Lego bricks in a staggered pattern to cover a small percentage of the area and he finds z_0 increases. As more and more bricks are added, the surface roughness (z_0) increases until 25 % of the surface is covered (Lee and Soliman and Lee and Hussain, using a regular and not a staggered pattern, find that maximum z_0 occurs for a coverage of about 15 %). On addition of more bricks, the cells on the floor become small enough to contain vortices, so that the flow begins to move over the bricks without reaching ground level between each one. The effective surface roughness begins to drop and with further additions of bricks drops further until, with bricks covering the whole ground, the surface roughness is back to its original value. But the whole ground has been displaced a distance into the flow equal to the height of the bricks. Provided that this is a small distance compared to the height of the wind tunnel, the velocity profile will be identical to the original one, except that the zero velocity point is above ground level. This distance is called the zero plane displacement and eqn. (8.16) is often rewritten

$$V = (U^*/k)\{\ln[(z - d)/z_0] + A(z - d)\} \tag{8.19}$$

where d is called the zero plane displacement. The value of d is shown by Thom [46] to vary with block height, side aspect ratio and plan density. As these variables are not always known, ESDU [16] suggest that an approximate value is used in all instances and this is given by

$$d = h - 2{\cdot}5z_0 \tag{8.20}$$

where *h* is the height of the surrounding buildings. This expression is based upon little evidence and is not universally accepted, although no other expression has been formulated which has received more widespread approval.

8.8. VERTICAL MIXING IN THE ATMOSPHERE

Static stability was discussed in Section 8.2 in terms of a lapse rate. Vertical mixing takes place as a result of turbulence and the appropriate term is the Reynolds stress, defined in eqn. (8.8). This vertical exchange of fluid tends to reduce temperature gradients and is consequently of great importance. The original log law presentation of the mean velocity profile (eqn. (8.10)) assumed that the shear stress was constant with height, which was originally assumed to apply to the lowest 30 m of the atmosphere only and forms the limiting condition at ground level for the equation expressing the mean velocity as a function of height (eqn. (8.15)).

Deaves and Harris [13] require a closing assumption to allow unique expressions for all functions and postulate that there is a parabolic variation of shear stress with height. Their justification is twofold: firstly it agrees with scant experimental observations in the atmosphere, and secondly it is obligatory on theoretical grounds if sensible conditions are applied to conditions at the gradient height ($z = H$). This gives the expression for the variation of shear stress with height as

$$\tau(z) = \rho U^{*2}[1 - (z/H)]^2 \qquad (8.21)$$

This leads to a very important simplification: in the lower atmosphere ($z < 200$ m) the mixing varies as U^{*2}, which by eqn. (8.14), varies with V_G. Thus in strong winds, usually those whose hourly average speed at 10 m height is greater than 10 m s^{-1}, U^{*2} is sufficient to produce enough mixing to ensure a neutrally stable layer. This has two interrelated implications— the first is that stability is not a parameter in the presentation of strong wind data and the second is that wind tunnel experiments representing strong wind conditions can be carried out with no attempts at thermal stratification.

In some examples of pollution from chimney emissions, the greatest ground level concentrations can be found close to the chimney when low windspeed and inversion conditions (see Section 8.3) prevail. This situation is extremely difficult to model in the wind tunnel, as explained in Chapter 10 of Volume 1.

9

Meteorology: Mean Windspeeds at One Point in Space

The term 'mean' denotes a time average, so the period over which the average is computed ought to be stated. In meteorological practice this is usually one hour. There is a very good reason for the choice of this value in that the spectrum of wind turbulence (such as the famous one by Van der Hoven [48] shown in Fig. 9.1) shows very little energy over the frequency range 1/1200 Hz to 1/7200 Hz. This is called the 'spectral gap', and means that the hourly average windspeed is a very stable quantity to calculate between these averaging times.

In many Codes of Practice around the world (for example BSI [5]) a gust speed (or 3 second average windspeed) is used. This averaging time has no particular relevance to the building scene, but represents the fastest response of standard anemometers of a few years ago. This gust speed approach was acceptable in the days when all wind loading could be considered quasi-static. With the advent of taller, more flexible buildings, dynamic response has achieved greater significance and the problem of separating the turbulence in the approaching wind and turbulence injected into the wind by the building itself is difficult. If the hourly average windspeed is used, which includes all frequencies less than 1/3600 Hz, and all higher frequencies are attributed to the pressure or force coefficients measured in wind tunnels with the correct spectrum of approaching wind, or correctly specified in Codes of Practice, then the two parts are uncorrelated and joint probabilities for a given value of pressure or force can be correctly estimated by eqn. (2.53). Modern Codes of Practice are reverting to the use of the hourly average windspeed.

In these volumes the slack use of the term 'mean windspeed' will always mean the 'hourly average windspeed'.

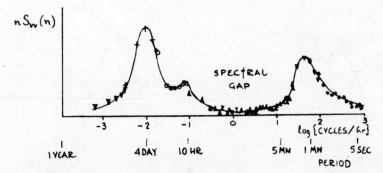

Fig. 9.1. Spectral density function for windspeed due to Van der Hoven.

9.1. EFFECT OF GEOGRAPHY

The major driving force for the wind occurs at gradient height and, as the linear scale of weather systems is large compared to cities and the stretches of countryside between, it is reasonable to assume that the gradient windspeed only changes slowly over the earth. This slow change is shown in Fig. 9.2, which is a map showing contours of the 'Meteorological Standard Windspeed'; the difference between this windspeed and the gradient windspeed is explained in Section 9.2.

The form of the variation of hourly average windspeed with height was derived in eqn. (8.12) which, when allowance for the zero plane displacement is made, becomes

$$V = (U^*/k)[\ln (\tilde{z}/z_0) + f_2(\tilde{z}/H)] \tag{9.1}$$

where

$$\tilde{z} = z - d \tag{9.2}$$

and d is defined by eqn. (8.20).

By eqn. (8.13), the ratio of the gradient windspeed to the frictional velocity is known (as z_0 and U^* are related). It is therefore possible to measure the windspeed close to the ground at location A (see Fig. 9.3) at which the surface roughness is known, and from these measurements to predict the gradient windspeed. On the assumption that the gradient windspeed does not change significantly over 20 or 30 miles, it is possible to develop the hourly average profile downwards from gradient height over a different type of terrain at location B. This operation is important, because most measurements are made over airfields which are, by definition, flat,

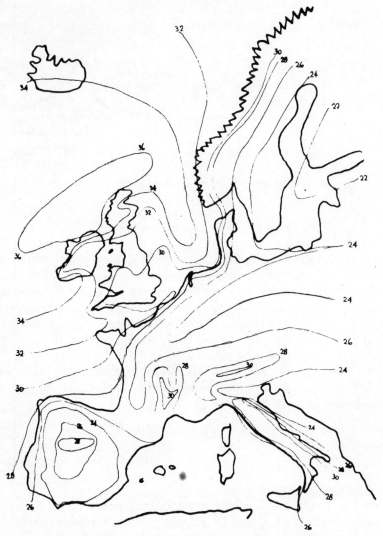

Fig. 9.2.   Map of Europe with isotachs of meteorological standard windspeed.

open, level spaces, but profiles of windspeed are mostly required over towns and cities where measurements are seldom made consistently for that length of time which would allow extreme value analysis to be conducted on the measurements to obtain design values of windspeed.

This process is used in the ESDU data sheet [16], although it is not clear

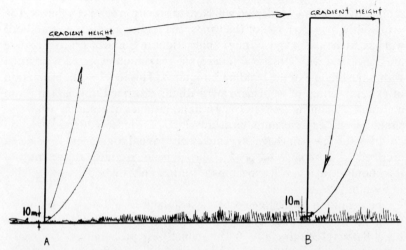

Fig. 9.3. Sketch showing method of calculating the variation of hourly average windspeed over one type of terrain when the variation is known over a different but local type of terrain.

from the text of the Data Item. In this operation it is essential to use the full eqn. (8.15) and not the simplified form (8.16) when working close to the gradient height.

There are some situations where it is advisable not to take the closest meteorological station as the crow flies as the basis for calculation of hourly average windspeeds at a required location. These are situations where the geography of the earth's surface has large features which affect winds up to gradient height. In these situations the closest meteorological station within the same airstream ought to be used. Sheffield is an example of such a situation. If in doubt the Meteorological Office ought to be consulted.

9.2. METEOROLOGICAL STANDARD WINDSPEED

Gradient windspeed is removed from the winds experienced by people walking around on the ground and, as a result, their magnitude is difficult to appreciate. The world meteorological community present windspeeds close to the ground and, because the windspeed has been measured by anemometers positioned upon masts usually at a height of 10 m (33 ft) above the surface, this height has been accepted as the standard.

The variation of windspeed with height, given in eqn. (8.15), is dependent upon surface roughness (z_0 and U^*), so a standard condition with which to replace the gradient windspeed will have to specify ground roughness. The probability of occurrence of the windspeed (either gradient or standard) will have to be stated and, as most applications in Codes of Practice to date are concerned with structural failure, the maximum expected windspeed within the lifetime of the building is required. This requires the estimation of extreme values of windspeed by methods described in Chapter 5 and considered again in Section 9.7. To date, insufficient research work and simultaneous experimental measurements of windspeed and direction covering too few years have prevented a directional component from being ascribed to extreme windspeeds. This is being rectified at present and directional estimates will appear in the future. This will be discussed further in Section 9.8.

The definition of the 'meteorological standard windspeed' can now be made as 'the windspeed averaged over one hour, measured 10 m above open, flat, level country $(z_0 = 0 \cdot 01 \text{ m})$ which has a probability of 1/50 that it will be exceeded in any year'. This can blow from any direction. Early tables used a roughness height (z_0) of $0 \cdot 003 \text{ m}$, but this has now been standardised at the simpler value of $0 \cdot 01 \text{ m}$.

9.3.   CHANGE OF SURFACE ROUGHNESS

In Section 9.1 the method whereby the low-level winds measured at location A are converted into a gradient windspeed, transferred unaltered to location B and then converted to low-level windspeeds over a different surface roughness is described (see Fig. 9.3). This assumes that the velocity profile over both types of roughness is in equilibrium; that is to say it is consistent with the surface roughness over its whole height.

Consider the wind which, after blowing for a hundred kilometres over the sea, reaches the coast and proceeds over a town. At first, the change of surface roughness can only affect the lower layers of the atmosphere, as shown in Fig. 9.4, and the profile will gradually change from the ground upwards until, provided the new surface roughness stretches unaltered for a sufficient distance downwind, the whole velocity profile will be appropriate to the new surface roughness.

Equation (8.14) relates the gradient height to the local surface roughness height and Deaves and Harris quote a value of 6 for β. It is obvious that a sudden change in z_0 will only affect the surface layers at the change of roughness, gradually affecting more and more of the boundary layer the further the location is downwind of the change of roughness. Taylor [44]

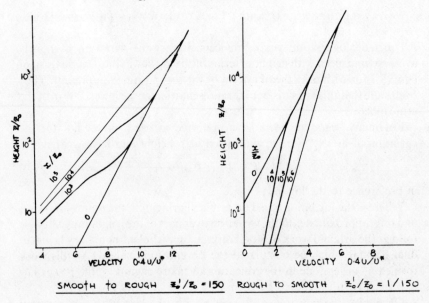

Fig. 9.4. Kinks in variation of hourly average windspeed due to changes of terrain upwind.

considered a sudden change of self-similar roughness both theoretically and in a wind tunnel. Several measurements have been made in the atmosphere; for example, Jones, de Larringa and Wilson [27] in studies over Liverpool suggest that 6 km fetch is required to change the profile up to 200 m height. Prasad and Panofsky [41] suggest that the internal boundary layer grows with a height to fetch ratio of 1:10. Panofsky and Petersen [37] describe an interesting set of experiments. Windspeeds are measured at various heights at Rijo which is on an isthmus. For some wind directions the fetch is over the sea; for another over land; for yet another, over sea then land then sea. Kinks are evident in the various profiles and these can be associated with the changes in ground roughness upwind.

Pasquill [38] presents similar data in a different form; he specifies a 'footprint' on the ground which will affect wind conditions at a stated point in the atmosphere. This approach not only specifies the kink in Fig. 9.4, but also allows an aerodynamicist who is simulating a boundary layer in the wind tunnel to determine where to change his simulation to correct that part which is insufficiently accurate.

Deaves is currently working on a theoretical representation of the change of roughness.

9.4. Variation with Height—The Log Law and the Power Law

All meteorologists and wind engineers discuss the variation of hourly average windspeed with height in terms of the log law in the general form of eqn. (9.1) or with only the first term of the second function present. They both state that this is a satisfactory representation of the lowest 200 m of the atmosphere.

For many years engineers have preferred to use a power law for the variation of hourly average windspeed with height and have written

$$V = V_{ref}(z/z_{ref})^{\alpha} \qquad (9.3)$$

in preference to the log law.

Whereas the log law is based on physical principles, the power law is not and only approximates to the variation over part of the height range. Its use follows the original work of Von Karman on turbulent boundary layers in ducts, about which he postulated the 'seventh-power law'. As this work formed a cornerstone in the education of many engineers, the power law approach is still favoured by them.

Originally, the power was adjusted to give the best fit to experimental data. In recent years, following the presentation of data by ESDU in 1972 and the work of Deaves and Harris more recently, both of whom used a 'log law plus' approach, modern power law values have been best fits to the 'log law plus' expressions over a limited height range (Deaves and Harris use a least squares fit over the height range 10–200 m).

Great care should be exercised in using the power law at the extremities of its fitted range. It is not unusual for a zero plane displacement to be greater than the height of surrounding buildings in some published values of the power index.

9.5. Ekman Spiral

In his study of the outer part of the atmospheric boundary layer (now called the Ekman layer), Ekman demonstrated that the direction of the hourly average windspeed varied with height. This is a direct consequence of the Reynolds stresses in the layer, and now that Deaves and Harris have postulated their closing assumption for the shear stress (eqn. (8.21)) the value of the spiral angle at gradient height (θ_0) can be expressed mathematically as

$$\sin \theta_0 = 2\beta U^*/V_G \qquad (9.4)$$

The spiral angle at any height z can be calculated from a partial differential equation, but Deaves and Harris suggest that a linear solution of the form

$$\theta = \theta_0(z/H) \tag{9.5}$$

gives sufficient accuracy for all practical purposes.

This spiral is usually ignored in all practical calculations.

9.6. PROBABILITY DENSITY FUNCTION FOR HOURLY AVERAGE WINDSPEEDS

As the hourly average windspeed varies with time, it must have a probability density function associated with it; one must not be confused by the term 'mean windspeed', which does not suggest variation with time, but means 'hourly average windspeed'. One of the boundary conditions for a boundary layer is that the vertical velocity at the surface is zero; it would appear logical to suggest that the windspeed close to the ground is composed of two uncorrelated Gaussian variables, u and v. Its probability distribution would therefore approximate to a Rayleigh one (Section 2.11). This was suggested by Davenport [10], and subsequent comparison with measurements has confirmed this suggestion.

Mayne [33] suggested that variations in topography produce distributions which depart on either side of the Rayleigh distribution, and recommended

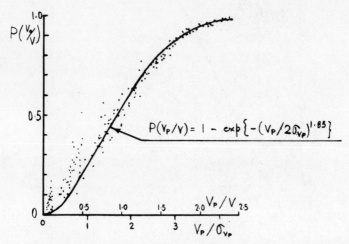

$$P(V_P/V) = 1 - \exp\left\{-(V_P/2\hat{\sigma}_{V_P})^{1.85}\right\}$$

Fig. 9.5. Cumulative distribution function for measured hourly average windspeeds at 35 stations in the UK.

that the use of a Weibull distribution (Section 2.9) gave an additional parameter in the form of the slope k which could be varied from site to site to obtain a better correspondence with measured values, the values straddling $k = 2$ which is the value at which the Weibull and Rayleigh distributions are identical. Figure 9.5 from Penwarden and Wise [40] shows the good agreement for 35 stations in the UK [25] with a Weibull distribution with $k = 1.85$ drawn through the points. There is scatter at the lower-windspeed end of the scale and Mayne suggests that this could be due to the insensitivity of the anemometer at these windspeeds.

Collingbourne [6] uses a three-constant Weibull distribution (eqn. (2.29)) and obtains good agreement even at low windspeeds (see Fig. 9.6). This

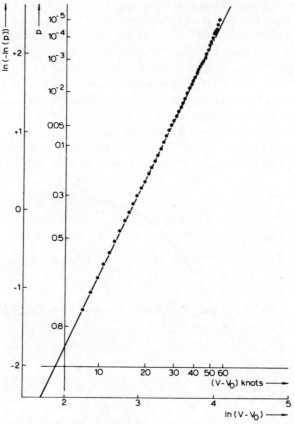

Fig. 9.6. Comparison between the Weibull distribution and measured hourly average windspeeds at valley (reproduced from Collingbourne [6]).

good agreement does not negate Mayne's suggestion that this is aliasing by the anemometer and not a feature of the windspeed itself.

These distributions are called the 'parent' distributions in the next section.

9.7. EXTREME VALUES OF WINDSPEED FOR DESIGN PURPOSES

In some design calculations, notably of a strength or stiffness nature, the value of windspeed which has a given probability of just not occurring during a very long period (50 years) is required. This value is far down the tail of the curve of the probability density function for the parent distribution described in the last section. Extreme value analysis techniques described in Chapter 5 are used to obtain values of this type.

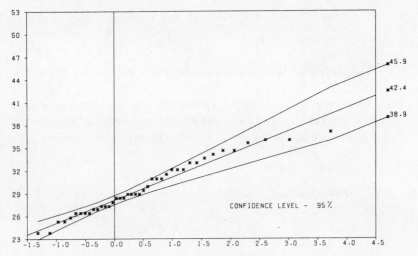

Fig. 9.7.   Extreme value analysis for windspeeds at Cranwell for 41 years (based on data from Hardman *et al.* [22]).

Because the parent distribution described in the last section is of the form of eqn. (5.10), then the extreme value distribution will be Fisher–Tippett type I. Shellard's [42] early work on wind (based on that of Gumbel [20]) followed the method outlined in Section 5.5 and produced results such as Figs. 9.7 and 9.8, in which the extreme windspeed is plotted as a function of the reduced variate.

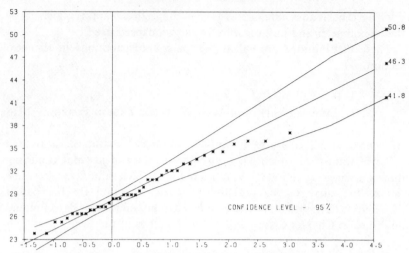

Fig. 9.8. Extreme value analysis for windspeeds at Cranwell for 42 years including the reading for 17 December 1952 (data from Hardman *et al.* [22]).

9.8. Frequency of Windspeed and Direction of Normal Windspeed

The estimation of the suitability of a pedestrian precinct for use depends on the daily conditions in that area, with possible differentials for day/night-time and for the different months of the year. In statistical terms this can be written

$$P(V_1, V_2; \theta_1, \theta_2) = \text{Prob}\,[V_1 \leq V < V_2; \theta_1 \leq \theta < \theta_2]$$

$$= \int_{V_1}^{V_2} \int_{\theta_1}^{\theta_2} p(V, \theta)\, \mathrm{d}\theta\, \mathrm{d}V$$

This 'joint probability' has been measured for many parts of the world (the data for 38 stations are presented as Table X in [25], from which Fig. 9.9 is reproduced; similar data are available from many Meteorological Offices in other countries) for windspeeds up to Beaufort force 12 (see Section 9.12 for a description).

This format of data is ideal for wind environment studies (see Chapter 12 of Volume 1) but there is one point worth bearing in mind when trying to improve such data, applied to a site at a distance from that from which the original data were obtained. The details of the measurement site should

Mean wind speed	Percentage number of hours with winds from												All directions
knots m.p.h.	350° 010°	020° 040°	050° 070°	080° 100°	110° 130°	140° 160°	170° 190°	200° 220°	230° 250°	260° 280°	290° 310°	320° 340°	Total
					DECEMBER								
Calm													2.6
1-3 1-3													21.7
4-6 4-7	0.5	0.3	0.2	0.2	0.8	0.8	0.5	0.9	5.2	5.7	2.4	0.7	18.2
7-10 8-12	0.6	0.9	0.3	0.4	1.1	1.0	0.7	1.8	6.0	4.3	1.8	0.5	19.4
11-16 13-18	0.3	0.8	0.6	0.6	1.2	0.8	0.7	2.6	6.3	3.6	0.9	0.3	18.7
17-21 19-24	0.1	0+	0.5	0.7	0.8	0.3	0.3	1.7	3.8	2.0	0.5	0.2	10.9
22-27 25-31		0+	0.5	0.3	0.6	0.2	0.1	0.5	2.4	1.2	0.3	0+	6.1
28-33 32-38		0+	0.1	0+	0.4	0+	0+	0.2	0.8	0.3	0+	0+	1.8
34-40 39-46			0.1		0.3	0.1		0+	0.1	0+	0.1	0+	0.7
41-47 47-54													
48-55 55-63													
56-63 64-72													
>63 >72													
TOTAL	1.5	2.0	2.3	2.2	5.2	3.2	2.3	7.7	24.6	17.1	6.0	1.7	100.1
Percentage number of hours missed													0
					YEAR								
Calm													2.7
1-3 1-3													24.6
4-6 4-7	0.7	1.0	1.3	1.8	1.8	0.9	0.6	1.2	4.3	4.6	1.7	0.9	20.8
7-10 8-12	0.8	1.1	1.5	2.4	1.9	1.0	0.8	1.8	5.1	4.5	1.9	0.9	23.7
11-16 13-18	0.5	0.9	1.3	1.5	1.1	0.9	0.6	1.6	4.7	3.8	1.5	0.8	19.2
17-21 19-24	0.1	0.1	0.4	0.3	0.3	0.3	0.2	0.6	1.8	1.5	0.5	0.2	6.3
22-27 25-31	0+	0+	0.1	0.1	0.2	0.1	0+	0.2	0.7	0.5	0.2	0+	2.1
28-33 32-38	0+	0+	0+	0+	0.1	0+	0+	0+	0.2	0.1	0+	0+	0.4
34-40 39-46			0+	0+	0+	0+		0+	0+	0+	0+	0+	0+
41-47 47-54													
48-55 55-63													
56-63 64-72													
>63 >72													
TOTAL	2.1	3.1	4.6	6.1	5.4	3.2	2.2	5.4	16.8	15.0	5.8	2.8	99.8
Percentage number of hours missed													0.2

Fig. 9.9. Table of windspeed and direction for December and for the year for Leuchars (from HMSO [25]).

always be stated so that a value of height z and surface roughness z_0 can be estimated or, better still, be stated. Averaging times for the readings are not always equal to one hour and should also be stated. With this information, various correction methods such as those given by ESDU [16] will allow the measured windspeeds to be related to the meteorological standard windspeed.

This has allowed for the difference between the surface roughnesses of the measuring and using stations. Large geographical features such as valleys also have an effect but over a greater distance, and are not allowed for by corrections to the surface roughness. To allow for such features, recourse must be made to further data available from each meteorological station which produces data such as Fig. 9.9 (for the UK this is presented in Tables of Surface Windspeed and Direction over the UK [25]). Each station publishes predictions of the meteorological standard windspeed for its site (Hardman *et al.* [22] for the UK). This value can be compared with the value from the map of the locality with isotachs marked (such as Fig. 9.2), from which all local effects have been removed. It is possible to compute a ratio of station to map reference windspeed and all other windspeeds can be multiplied by the same ratio to correct for a 'normal' site.

If the site for which the data are required is sheltered or exposed, further corrections should be applied as a further amendment to the original data to make it more appropriate to the particular site.

9.9. EFFECT OF WIND DIRECTION ON EXTREME VALUES OF WINDSPEED

In the last section the bivariate tables of windspeed and direction were discussed and applied to wind environment studies. In wind loading studies values of extreme windspeeds (usually in the form of the meteorological standard windspeed) are used and it would obviously lead to savings if this extreme value windspeed could be specified for different wind directions. Unfortunately, insufficient data are available at the present date for this to be done. The reason is that the principle of the extreme value analysis described in Chapter 5 is that it gives approximations to the 'tails' of the distributions of the parent distributions. For the data presented in Fig. 9.9 for winds from the North ($345°$–$015°$) the total percentage of the time was $2\cdot1$, or an average of 184 h in the year. The highest windspeed would have a probability of about $\frac{1}{16}$ (as $v < 0\cdot1$). This could hardly be described as being in the tail of the distribution and extensions from this value could be misleading.

Research work is in progress [6] to fulfil this need as it could bring considerable economic gains.

9.10.   EFFECT OF AVERAGING TIME

The effect of the limiting frequency response of the anemometer measuring the windspeed is given in eqn. (3.35) for the general case. The derivation of

Table 9.1. *Beaufort scale*

Beaufort range	Hourly average windspeed limits of ranges (m s^{-1})	Description of wind	At sea	Noticeable effect of wind — On land
0	<0·45	Calm	Sea is mirror-smooth	Smoke rises vertically
1	0·45–1·55	Light	Small wavelets like scales, but no foam crests	Direction shown by smoke drift but not by vanes
2	1·55–3·35	Light	Waves are short and more pronounced	Wind felt on face: leaves rustle: windvanes moved
3	3·35–5·60	Light	Crests begin to break: foam has glassy appearance, not as yet white	Leaves and twigs in motion: wind extends a light flag
4	5·60–8·25	Moderate	Waves are longer: many white horses	Raises dust and loose paper and moves small branches
5	8·25–10·95	Fresh	Waves are more pronounced: white foam crests seen everywhere	Small trees in leaf begin to sway
6	10·95–14·10	Strong	Larger waves form: foam crests more extensive	Large branches begin to move: telephone wires whistle
7	14·10–17·20	Strong	Sea heaps up: foam begins to blow in streaks	Whole trees in motion
8	17·20–20·80	Gale	Waves increase visibly: foam is blown in dense streaks	Twigs break off: progress generally impeded
9	20·80–24·35	Gale	High waves with long overhanging crests: great foam patches	Slight structural damage occurs: chimney pots removed
10	24·35–28·40	Strong gale	Waves so high that ships within sight are hidden in the troughs: sea covered with streaky foam:	Trees uprooted: considerable structural damage
11	28·40–32·40	Storm	Air filled with spray	Damage is widespread: seldom experienced in England
12	>32·40	Hurricane		Countryside is devastated: winds of this force are encountered only in tropical revolving storms

windspeeds based upon larger averaging times than the measurements are frequently required. Fortunately, it is found that the spectrum of temperate strong winds approximates to a unique curve (see Section 11.1) so that eqn. (3.35) can be integrated. This form is difficult to apply and ESDU [16] gives a simple expression whereby it may be calculated.

9.11.   Effect of Sample Length

Van der Hoven's spectrum for a number of sites, including Brookhaven, is reproduced from Van der Hoven [48] as Fig. 9.1, and mention of the spectral gap has already been made in the introduction to this chapter. ESDU found that extreme values calculated from samples of windspeed of durations shorter than 45 min tended to show lower values as the sample length decreased. Deacon presents data for Sale [12] and Helliwell for London [24] which suggest that the extrapolation expressions derived in ESDU [16] can be applied to samples as short as 5 min. The problems of sample length are analysed in Section 3.10.

9.12.   Beaufort Scale

In 1805 Admiral Sir Francis Beaufort encountered the problem of determining with some degree of accuracy the windspeed at sea with only sailors having no scientific background to carry out the measurements. He defined ranges of windspeed, in each of which some describable feature could be attributed to either the sea or the sails of the ships. With one skilled sailor he measured the windspeed (his averaging time is unrecorded) for each occurrence and determined values of windspeed at the limits of each range, which he numbered from 0 (calm) to 12 (hurricane). He gave terms to each range (11 is called 'storm') as well as a description of the behaviour of some part of the sea or ship. In a 'Wind Effects on Buildings' context descriptions of sea and ship are out of place, so new descriptions created by Sir George Simpson when Director of the Meteorological Office in the UK have been added in what is sometimes called a 'land Beaufort scale'. Over the years the numerical values defining the limits of the ranges have changed slightly, as they do from country to country. However, the World Meteorological Organisation has agreed values and these are presented in Table 9.1.

10

Meteorology: Amplitudes of Windspeed Fluctuations at One Point in Space

Chapter 2 explained how amplitudes of fluctuations are best described quantitatively by means of the probability density function. These ideas are now expanded with direct application to windspeed.

10.1. MOMENTS OF THE PROBABILITY DENSITY FUNCTION

An attempt to express information about the amplitude of windspeed fluctuations in several discrete numbers uses the moments of the probability density function (Section 2.1). The first moment gives the mean value, which was discussed exhaustively in Chapter 9. The second moment of the windspeed, with its mean value removed, gives the 'variance', whose positive square root is equal to the standard deviation. This value is central to most data on turbulence.

A new term is often used—the 'intensity of turbulence'. This is a non-dimensional measure of the standard deviation and is defined as

$$I_i(z) = \sigma_i(z)/V(z) \qquad (10.1)$$

The suffix i has been added to denote that the three components of turbulence each have a standard deviation and an intensity of turbulence, though they are all made non-dimensional by the mean windspeed. Should the suffix be omitted, convention would suggest that the u component of turbulence is quoted.

The higher moments are rarely quoted in open literature, but the values are used in research literature; in particular a value of kurtosis is often presented to demonstrate how an experimental distribution differs from a Gaussian one (kurtosis = 3 for a Gaussian distribution).

10.2. Variation of Turbulence Intensity with Height

The standard deviation of component i (which can be u, v or w) of turbulence is written as σ_i. A similar procedure to that used in Chapter 8 for the mean windspeed ought to apply, in which a law of the wall and a law of the wake are defined. A generalised matching expression is then defined which has the first two laws expressed mathematically as limiting expressions.

This application of the similarity law gives constant values for σ_i/U^*. Numerical values of (2·1 to 2·9), (1·3 to 2·6) and 1·25 were originally allocated for σ_u/U^*, σ_v/U^* and σ_w/U^*.

More recent measurements have shown that σ_u/U^* is a function of z_0, which explains the range of values measured for the 'constants'. If therefore σ_i/U^* were written

$$\sigma_i/U^* = (1/k)[\ln(z/z_0) + f_2(z/H)] \tag{10.2}$$

in a form very similar to that for the mean windspeed (eqn. (8.12)), the intensity of turbulence (defined as $I_i = \sigma_i/V$) could then be written

$$I_i = [\ln(z/z_0) + f_2(z/H)]$$

ESDU wrote this in function form:

$$I_i = f(z, z_0)$$

and produced [16] empirical relationships by fitting all available data. Deaves and Harris [13] attempted to find the equations for the inner and outer parts of the layer and suggested that they were

$$\sigma_u/U^* = K_1[1 - (z/H)] \qquad \text{for the outer region}$$
$$\sigma_u/U^* = K_2 \ln(z/z_0) \qquad \text{for the inner region}$$

These eventually give rise to the fitting expression

$$\sigma_u/U^* = 2·63\eta[0·538 + 0·09\ln(z/z_0)]^{\eta^{16}} \tag{10.3}$$

where $\eta = 1 - (z/H)$.

There is a height near the ground at which this expression gives a maximum value of turbulence; a simpler expression for this height is suggested by Deaves and Harris as

$$z_m/H = 0·44 R_0^{-1/4} \tag{10.4}$$

where
$$R_0 \equiv \text{surface Rossby number}$$
$$= U^*/f z_0 = \beta H/z_0 \tag{10.5}$$

Equation (10.3), taken in conjunction with the equation for mean windspeed (eqn. (8.15)), gives a value for the intensity of turbulence which is not independent of U^* but depends only weakly on surface Rossby number.

10.3.   GUST SPEEDS—EFFECT OF AVERAGING TIME ON THE VALUE OF WINDSPEED

Figure 10.1 shows a sample of windspeed taken from a measuring instrument whose averaging time is zero. It is explained in Section 3.10 that the effect of using an instrument with a finite averaging time is to reduce the amplitude of the signal in the higher frequency ranges. The relationship is given in eqn. (3.34) where

$$u(t, n, s) = u(t, n, 0)(\sin \pi ns)/\pi ns$$

and the effect is shown graphically in Fig. 3.11. In practice, the effect is equivalent to applying a frequency-dependent filter to the values of windspeed.

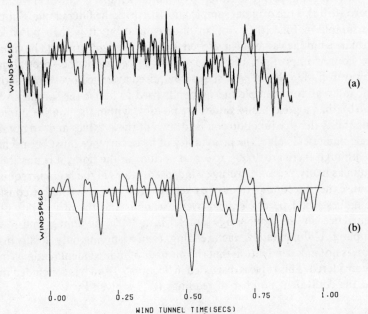

Fig. 10.1.   Variation of wind tunnel windspeed with time: (a) filtered at 400 Hz; (b) filtered at 50 Hz.

The effect of requiring a value of windspeed which has a given averaging time is identical to measuring that windspeed with an instrument which has that averaging time. If the spectrum of the windspeed is as shown in Fig. 10.2(a) (this is described in greater detail in Chapter 11), and the filter for averaging time s (shown originally as Fig. 3.11) is repeated in Fig. 10.2(b), the spectrum of the windspeed averaged over 3 seconds is shown in Fig. 10.2(c).

Equation (3.10) shows that the definition of the spectral density function requires that the variance is the integral of the function over the whole frequency range, so that

$$\sigma_u^2 = \int_0^\infty S_{uu}(n)\,\mathrm{d}n \qquad (10.6)$$

and therefore the variance of the windspeed averaged over s seconds will be less than that for the basic windspeed evaluated from an instrument whose averaging time is less than 's' seconds, the amount of reduction depending on the relative position, in frequency terms, of the curves in Figs. 10.2(a) and 10.2(b).

The effect of applying the filter to the actual sample is shown in Fig. 10.1, where 10.1(a) is the original sample and 10.1(b) is the filtered one. Suppose the sample in Fig. 10.1 is of an hour's duration; it is then possible to evaluate a unique value of windspeed for each averaging time. (The value of one hour is important, because it is in the centre of the spectral gap.) However, if the value of windspeed is required averaged over some shorter time interval, for example the s seconds used to derive the sample in Fig. 10.1(b), then a great many values are possible within the hour's sample. A probability density function can be drawn of these values and, to obtain a single numerical value, the probability of its occurrence must be specified.

Although there are $3600/s$ s second periods in the hour, it is possible to obtain as many s second average windspeed values in the hour as required, because the 's' second periods can overlap. However, it is usual to consider the highest windspeed averaged over s seconds and the probability of its occurrence in an hour-long sample is $s/3600$, assuming end-to-end sampling. Unfortunately, each reading, even assuming only $3600/s$ in the hour, is not independent, so that the number of independent readings must be considered. This topic is discussed in Section 5.7 and it is concluded there that the equivalent number of readings (N_e) is given by

$$N_e = 3600\,v/s$$

where v is defined by eqn. (5.22).

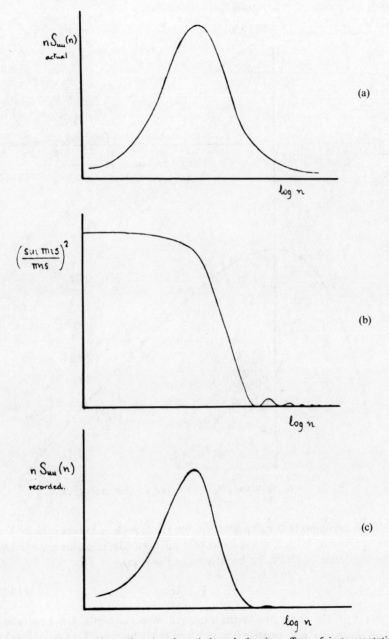

Fig. 10.2. Spectral density function for windspeed showing effect of instrumentation averaging time: (a) correct spectral density function; (b) instrumentation admittance function; (c) measured spectral density function.

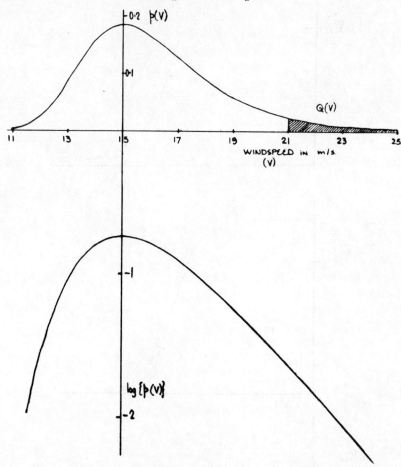

Fig. 10.3. Probability density function for gust windspeeds.

If the probability density function for the sample is known, shown for example in Fig. 10.3, then the value of windspeed which has the probability of exceedence of $Q(\hat{V})$ can be written in the form

$$\hat{V}_s = V + k\sigma_{V,s} \qquad (10.7)$$

where $\hat{V}_s$ is the peak gust speed averaged over s seconds, k is dependent upon the probability density function and the value of $Q(\hat{V}_s)$ and $\sigma_{V,s}$ is the standard deviation of the windspeed averaged over s seconds.

Because $\sigma_{V,s}$ is related to σ_V provided a unique spectral density function applies, it is possible to rewrite eqn. (10.7) as

$$\hat{V}_s = V + k'\sigma_V \tag{10.8}$$

where k' is now also a function of s and σ_V is independent of s. For high windspeeds $(V > 10 \, \mathrm{m \, s^{-1}})$ for which the atmosphere is neutrally stable, eqn. (10.8) is rewritten

$$\hat{V}_s = V(1 + k'\sigma_V/V) \tag{10.9}$$

and ESDU [16] give an empirical expression for the term in the parentheses derived from measured results.

Harris and Deaves [13], on the other hand, go back to eqn. (10.7) and quote

$$\hat{V}_{3s} = V + 3\cdot7\sigma_{V,3s} \tag{10.10}$$

based on measurements with an anemomograph, which contains both the anemometer and recording instrument and has a response time of 3 seconds.

In work originating in Canada [49], the term 'gust factor' is used. This is simply the ratio of gust speed to mean windspeed and is equal to the term in the parentheses of eqn. (10.9). Its use is discussed by Mayne [15] with the conclusion that it is not a particularly useful concept.

10.4. CHOICE OF AVERAGING TIME—THE *TVL* FORMULA

The shorter the averaging time, the larger will be the value of gust speed; experimental measurements of this are presented in Durst [14]. Atmospheric turbulence can be considered as being composed of a whole range of eddies of all different sizes being carried past the observer by the mean windspeed. As the eddies pass, the windspeed rises and falls, the slow changes being caused by the passage of the large eddies and the rapid changes by the small eddies; many different sized eddies pass at a given instant in a variety of patterns.

To get good correlation of windspeed at two points as a single eddy passes, the distance between the two points must be smaller than the size of the eddy. When the turbulence is composed of a mixture of eddies, there is still this limiting size of eddy, such that all larger eddies are correlated and all smaller eddies are not. In practice, the cut-off is not as sharp as this, there being a gradual loss in correlation over a range of sizes.

The size of the limiting eddy can be transformed into an averaging time or a frequency by the mean velocity with which the eddies are being transported past the observer. It is then possible to write an expression for the desired averaging time T in terms of the mean windspeed V and the separation L of the points. Thus

$$TV = LK \qquad (10.11)$$

where K is a constant depending upon the purpose for which the correlation is required and the degree of correlation acceptable. This is the fundamental TVL formula. Values of K for special applications are introduced in Volume 1 as applicable: for example, in Section 4.2 of Volume 1 for quasi-static wind loading.

11

Meteorology: Frequency of Windspeed Fluctuations at One Point in Space

It was argued in Chapter 3 that the most common way to present data concerning time or frequency is to use the spectral density function. Many workers have presented expressions for this function for all components of windspeed, the better known being Kolmogorov, Panofsky, Pasquill and Van der Hoven in the meteorological world and Von Karman, Davenport, Harris and ESDU in the engineering fraternity. All are similar, the meteorologists studying the life span of turbulence from creation to dissipation, and the engineers starting with these skeletons but with many measured spectra to hand, which differ considerably one with another, producing compromises which have the widest application.

The study of a family of spectra taken at the same site at different times when the wind is from the same rough direction, discussed by Davenport and Isyumov [11] and presented here as Fig. 11.1, should banish thoughts of a unique spectrum adhered to exactly at all times and in all places. The variations from place to place are of the same order as variations from time to time at one location, so that a unique best fit curve can be presented for strong winds when thermal stratification is negligible. For gentle winds, stability of the atmosphere must be introduced because it has an effect for which allowances can be made.

This chapter applies to strong winds when the stability of the atmosphere can be assumed to be neutral. This is the condition applicable to structural design studies. For other conditions, the work of meteorologists (for example, Lumley and Panofsky [31] or Pasquill [39]) should be consulted.

It is not intended in this chapter to give a series of inter-related functions for all the quantities related to spectra. The reader should refer to publications whose sole purpose is to present such functions. The reader is referred in particular to the ESDU Data Items [17, 18] or Harris and Deaves [13] for up-to-date comprehensive sets of coherent data. Counihan

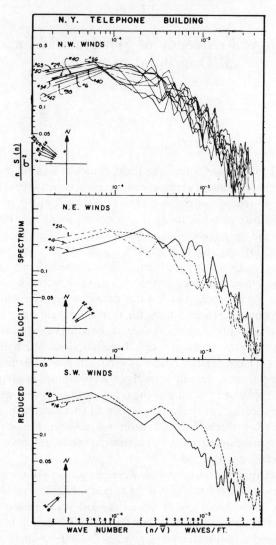

Fig. 11.1.   Temporal variations of spectral density function at one site (from Davenport [10]).

[8] historically presents the expressions suggested by various workers over the period 1880 to 1972.

11.1. THE NORMALISED SPECTRAL DENSITY FUNCTION

The spectral density function for winds $(S_{uu}(n))$ has dimensions of velocity squared, so that it could be made non-dimensional by dividing by the square of any velocity. A study of eqn. (3.11) would suggest that the most appropriate velocity squared is the variance of the windspeed. The term

$$S_{uu}(n)/\sigma_u^2 \qquad (11.1)$$

is often called the 'normalised spectral density function'. This quantity has the advantage that its integral over the frequency range is unity and is therefore comparable for all situations.

For the spectrum to have wide applicability, the frequency must also be made non-dimensional. In this respect there are differences between workers. In these volumes the works of ESDU and Deaves and Harris will be followed in that the non-dimensional frequency $(\tilde{n})$ is defined as

$$\tilde{n}(z, z_0) = n^x L_i(z, z_0)/V(z) \qquad (11.2)$$

where $^x L_i$ is the integral length for the i component of velocity measured in the x direction; the value of i is chosen to conform to the component of windspeed relating to the spectral density function. This is discussed further in Section 11.3.

Within the limits of repeatability in the atmosphere it is found possible to write

$$S_{uu}(n)/\sigma_u^2 = f[\tilde{n}(z, z_0)] \qquad (11.3)$$

where the function is different from worker to worker, but all agree that it becomes asymptotic to

$$S_{uu}(n)/\sigma_u^2 = K\tilde{n}^{-5/3} \qquad (11.4)$$

for high values of frequency. Normalised spectral density functions for the lateral and vertical components are also presented by many workers. These have a different function from that for longitudinal turbulence, but in the ESDU Data Items the function is the same for lateral and vertical turbulence provided the corresponding components are used for variances and integral scale lengths.

Prior to 1960 several forms of spectral density functions for representing atmospheric turbulence had been proposed, of which the Von Karman form was the best known. Davenport then proposed

$$nS_{uu}(n) = 4K(10)[V(10)]^2 \tilde{n} \phi(\tilde{n}) \qquad (11.5)$$

where $K(10)$ is the surface drag coefficient $= U^{*2}/[V(10)]^2$,
$V(10)$ is the mean windspeed at 10 m height,
$\tilde{n} = n\mathscr{L}/V(10)$, $\mathscr{L}$ is a length constant given the value 1200 m by Davenport and $\phi(\tilde{n})$ is a function derived to fit measured spectra and also to give the correct asymptotic value (eqn. (11.4)) at high frequencies.

This expression was modified by Harris [23] to become

$$nS_{uu}(n) = 4K(10)[V(10)]^2 \tilde{n}/(2 + \tilde{n}^2)^{5/6} \qquad (11.6)$$

As both these models give a value for the variance of the u component of windspeed which depends only upon mean windspeed and is independent of height, the use of the constant value of $\mathscr{L}$ was doubted. Deaves and Harris introduced a length scale which varied with height and realised that this length scale, the autocovariance function and the spectral density function are inter-related. A time scale $T(z)$ was defined in terms of the autocovariance coefficient (eqn. (3.7)) and its use in place of $\mathscr{L}/\bar{V}(10)$, which has the same units, gives

$$nS_{uu}(n, z) = 0.115\sigma_u^2(z)nT_u(z)/\{0.0141 + [nT_u(z)]^2\}^{5/6} \qquad (11.7)$$

and by equating this form to that obtained at high frequencies it was found possible to relate the time scale to the Kolmogorov parameter. The length scale $^xL_u(z)$ and the time scale $T_u(z)$ are related by the local mean windspeed $\bar{V}(z)$:

$$^xL_u(z) = T_u(z)V(z) \qquad (11.8)$$

so that the expression for the normalised spectrum becomes

$$nS_{uu}(n)/\sigma_u^2(z) = [0.115n^xL_u(z)/V(z)]/\{0.0141 + [n^xL_u(z)/V(z)]^2\}^{5/6}$$

$$(11.9)$$

Deaves and Harris were then able to evaluate the constants in eqn. (11.7) by independent measurements of two variations:

(i)   the variation of Kolmogorov parameter with height;
(ii) the variation of the ratio of length scales with height.

ESDU, on the other hand, plotted all the accredited experimental spectra, giving particular attention to the lengths of samples and the averaging times of the measuring instruments used, and found that the data could be collapsed into a single curve when a non-dimensional frequency was used. In Figs. 10 of Data Item 74031 [18] the scatter in the experimental data is shown. A modified form of the Von Karman spectrum gave the best fit to these data and the spectra are presented in the form of

$$nS_{uu}(n, z)/\sigma_u^2(z) = f\{\log [\tilde{n}(z, z_0)]\}$$

in place of eqn. (11.3).

11.2. AUTOCOVARIANCE FUNCTIONS

In eqn. (3.16) it is shown that the autocovariance and spectral density functions are related by the equation

$$C_{uu}(\tau) = \int_0^\infty S_{uu}(n) \cos 2\pi n\tau \, dn$$

so that, once the spectral density function is known, the autocovariance function can be derived. Before the advent of computers and the fast Fourier transformation, raw data were first converted into the autocovariance function and thence by the Fourier transformation to the spectral density function. This approach has many advantages in the physical understanding of phenomena although, in recent years due also to Davenport's wide use of spectra and the fact that a building's response to dynamic excitation is more easily understood in terms of frequency, the spectral approach is generally preferred.

The autocovariance coefficient for atmospheric turbulence can be related to a non-dimensional time lag by means of modified Bessel functions of the second kind of orders $\frac{1}{3}$ and $\frac{2}{3}$ (values of these functions are given by ESDU Reference [19]).

11.3. INTEGRAL SCALES

Integral length and time scales are discussed in general in Sections 4.9 and 4.10 and are related to the appropriate covariance coefficients by equations such as

$$T_u = \int_0^\infty c_{uu}(\tau) \, d\tau \qquad \text{(eqn. (4.17))}$$

$$^xL_u = \int_0^\infty (\sigma_{u,u_1}/\sigma_u)^2 \, dx \qquad \text{(eqn. (4.15))}$$

ESDU, having fitted a mathematical model for the u component spectrum, is able to derive an expression for the integral time and scale lengths in terms of z and z_0 [19] (for the other integral scale lengths see Section 12.5).

Deaves and Harris relate the two scales (u component in the x direction and time) by eqn. (11.8) and give an expression for the length scale as

$$^{x}L_u(z) = 0.48[B(z)]^{-3/2}\sigma_u^3(z)/\varepsilon(z) \tag{11.10}$$

where $B(z)$ is the correction factor for the Kolmogorov parameter

$$
\begin{aligned}
&= 1 && \text{for } z > z_c \\
&= [1 - (1 - z/z_0)^2]^{1/2} && \text{for } z < z_c
\end{aligned}
\Bigg\} \tag{11.11}
$$

$$z_c/H = 0.39(R_0)^{-1/8} \tag{11.12}$$

where R_0 is given by eqn. (10.5), H is given by eqn. (8.14), $\sigma_u(z)$ is given by eqn. (10.3) and $\varepsilon(z)$ is given by eqn. (11.13).

The time scale used in the spectral density function (eqn. (11.7)) is calculated from eqns. (11.8) and (11.10).

11.4. ENERGY DISSIPATION

The dissipation of velocity energy in the atmosphere is central to all studies of atmospheric turbulence and arises from the interaction of the Reynolds stress with the mean velocity gradient. In analytical form it is given by

$$\varepsilon(z) = \tau(z)\,dV(z)/dz \tag{11.13}$$

where

$$\tau(z) = \rho U^{*2}(1 - z/H)^2 \tag{11.14}$$

and $dV(z)/dz$ is obtained by differentiating eqn. (8.15).

In the process of the atmospheric boundary layer's existence, turbulence is continually being created by surface friction and the drag and wakes of bodies attached to the earth's surface; this turbulence is being dissipated by internal friction within the air and converted to heat. Equilibrium conditions occur when dissipation equals creation, but distances of homogeneous terrain roughness over land are usually too short for this balance to be achieved in practice.

12

Meteorology: Variations of Windspeed in Space

In the last four chapters a complete description of the windspeeds at a single point in space was given. This is sufficient for most purposes, but there are a few which require data about the instantaneous relationships between the windspeed at two points in space.

In the direction of the mean wind (x) there is a relationship between variations with distance and variations with time, which is encapsulated in Taylor's hypothesis. This postulates that the turbulence pattern is frozen into the wind, and space (x) and time (t) are related by the mean windspeed. This produces relationships such as eqn. (4.16).

This is a concept of turbulence as a random mixture of eddies of all shapes and sizes as if etched on a sheet of perspex, the perspex moving with the mean windspeed (see Fig. 12.1). An anemometer at point A would record exactly the same sample of turbulence as an anemometer at point B, only at an instant x/V seconds earlier. In practice, however, turbulence is continually being created and dissipated, often with a cascading of frequencies in between (i.e. created at a large scale and dissipated into heat at a very small scale). Thus this simple concept, which is sufficient in some circumstances, is not generally applicable and it would be wise to extend our understanding. In the case of cross-flow directions this does not work and the simplistic approach is to assume homogeneity to predict cross-wind parameters from the along-wind ones discussed above.

Section 2.17 and Chapter 4 of this volume define the terms which will be used for a full statistical description of the data. ESDU [19] and Teunissen [45] are the only sources known to the author of a complete set of coherent data on windspeeds at two points in space. Several PhD theses have presented limited data at two points in space. The succeeding sections will discuss the problem; the ESDU Data Item must be studied to obtain the expressions and numerical values. For simplicity of notation, the u

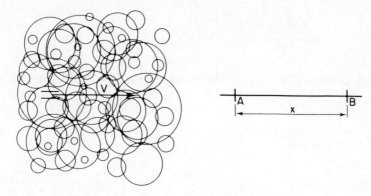

Fig. 12.1. Sketch showing eddy representation of turbulence passing measuring stations.

component of turbulence at locations 1 and 2 will be considered in Sections 12.1 to 12.3; other components of turbulence will be mentioned in Section 12.4.

12.1. AMPLITUDE DESCRIPTION—JOINT PROBABILITY DENSITY FUNCTIONS

Very few joint probability measurements have been made of windspeed in the atmosphere, so it is normal to use the Gaussian model which was explained in Section 2.15.

Let

$$z_1 = u_1(t)/\sigma_{u_1} \qquad (12.1)$$

and

$$z_2 = u_2(t)/\sigma_{u_2} \qquad (12.2)$$

then the joint probability function is given by eqn. (2.45):

$$p(z_1, z_2) = \frac{\exp\{[z_1^2 - 2c_{u_1 u_2}(0)z_1 z_2 + z_2^2]/[2(c_{u_1 u_2}^2(0) - 1)]\}}{2\pi[1 - c_{u_1 u_2}^2(0)]^{1/2}} \qquad (12.3)$$

To calculate this, z_1 and z_2 are derived from eqns. (12.1) and (12.2), but the cross covariance coefficient at zero time lag $c_{u_1 u_2}(0)$ defined in eqn. (4.3) is difficult to evaluate. Two methods are possible and these are considered in Section 12.3.

12.2.   FREQUENCY DESCRIPTION—COHERENCE FUNCTIONS

In the along-wind case the distance between locations 1 and 2 (Δx) can be converted into a time lag of $\Delta x/V$ if Taylor's hypothesis is accepted. When the cross spectral density function is expressed in polar form, as in eqn. (4.8), and the modulus of the cross spectral density function is converted into a coherence function by eqn. (4.11), Taylor's hypothesis would suggest that the coherence function would be unity.

The few data available suggest that, for V/n greater than about 300 m, the effects of the ground can be allowed for by the empirical expression

$$\gamma = \exp\left(-2\pi\,\Delta x/V\right) \tag{12.4}$$

The phase lag, defined in eqn. (4.10), can be calculated from the Taylor hypothesis to be

$$\theta = 2\pi n\,\Delta x/V \tag{12.5}$$

By using eqns. (4.9) to (4.11), the cospectrum and the quadspectrum can be calculated for the along-wind separation of the u-component of turbulence.

ESDU [19] present expressions for the co-coherence and quad-coherence of the u component of turbulence for lateral and vertical separations based upon the Von Karman spectral equations.

12.3.   CROSS COVARIANCE FUNCTIONS

The cross covariance function for zero time lag was required in eqn. (12.3) to calculate the joint probability density function. It would appear that it can be obtained from the inverse Fourier transform of eqns. (4.6a) and (4.7a):

$$C_{u_1 u_2}(\tau)_{\text{sym}} = \int_0^\infty P_{u_1 u_2}(n)\cos 2\pi n\tau \, \mathrm{d}n \tag{12.6}$$

and

$$C_{u_1 u_2}(\tau)_{\text{antisym}} = \int_0^\infty Q_{u_1 u_2}(n)\sin 2\pi n\tau \, \mathrm{d}n \tag{12.7}$$

when the complete cross covariance function $C_{uu}(\tau)$ is equal to the sum of the two parts

$$C_{u_1 u_2}(\tau) = C_{u_1 u_2}(\tau)_{\text{sym}} + C_{u_1 u_2}(\tau)_{\text{antisym}} \tag{12.8}$$

The cross covariance function for zero time lag is given by eqn. (12.6) and is

$$C_{u_1u_2}(0) = \int_0^\alpha P_{u_1u_2}(n)\,dn \qquad (12.9)$$

Unfortunately the expressions for the cospectrum derived in Section 12.2 proved impossible to integrate in general, although values for special cases can be obtained in this way.

However, it is possible, using Taylor's hypothesis, to derive the cross covariance function for zero lag directly from the autocovariance function of eqn. (3.3) with the time lag equated to $\Delta x/V$ for the along-wind case. Thus

$$C_{u_1u_2}(0) = C_{uu}(\tau) \qquad (12.10)$$

where

$$\tau = \Delta x/V$$

The inaccuracies introduced by using the Taylor hypothesis can be allowed for by modifying the displacement between the two locations considered (Δx) so that it no longer represents the actual distance between the locations. Further assumptions of isotropy allow other modifications to be applied to the corrections for cross-wind separation of the locations in question.

12.4. Cross-Wind Components of Turbulence

For simplicity of notation, the u component was discussed in Sections 12.1 to 12.3. Similar approaches are possible for the cross-wind components of turbulence when correct functions are used for the cross-spectral density functions and integral scale lengths. In the ESDU Data Item [19] data are confined to x and z separations for the v component and to x and y separations for the w component. No data are presented for cross velocities.

12.5. Integral Scale Lengths

By definition the integral scale lengths are related to the cross covariance function by the equation

$$^xL_u = \int_0^\infty c_{u_1u_2}(0)\,d(\Delta x) \qquad (12.11)$$

where locations 1 and 2 are displaced Δx in the x direction. This is identical to the definition given in eqn. (4.15), which has already been discussed in Section 11.3 for this integral scale length.

There are nine principal integral scale lengths composed of the three components of velocity and the three axial directions. Expressions for all nine are given in ESDU [19] in terms of z and z_0 for strong winds, and these are consistent with the spectra given in the same reference.

Deaves and Harris [13] present their expression for ${}^x L_u$ in eqn. (11.10) and, assuming isotropy, their value for a cross-wind integral scale length ${}^y L_u$ is

$$ {}^y L_u = 0{\cdot}24 [B(z)]^{-1/2} \sigma_u^3(z)/\varepsilon(z) \qquad (12.12) $$

Their expressions for both integral scale lengths can be shown to be functions of z, z_0 and V_G, which would agree with the ESDU expressions provided the variation with the gradient windspeed V_G is small for large values of V_G.

When separations are a mixture of separations in the principal axes, a compound length scale can be calculated from the principal integral scale lengths using a weighting depending upon the separations in the main directions. Expressions for these 'compound length scales' are given in ESDU [19].

References

1. Aanensen, C. J. M., 'Gales in Yorkshire in February 1962', *Meteorological Office Geophysical Memoirs No. 108 Met\O. 711c*, HMSO, London, 1965.
2. Abramowitz, M. and Stegun, I. A., *Handbook of Mathematical Functions*, Dover Publications, New York, 1968.
3. Bendat, J: S. and Piersol, A. G., *Random Data: Analysis and Measurement Procedures*, Wiley Interscience, New York, 1971.
4. Brinkworth, B. J., *An Introduction to Experimentation*, The English Universities Press Ltd, 1968.
5. *BSI CP3 Basic Data for the Design of Buildings, Chapter V, Loading; Part 2, Wind Loads*, Ch V, Pt 2, 1972.
6. Collingbourne, R. H., 'Wind data available in the meteorological office (UK),. *J. Indust. Aerodynamics*, **3**(2/3), July 1978, 145–56.
7. Counihan, J., 'Wind tunnel determination of the roughness length as a function of the fetch and the roughness density of 3D roughness elements', *Int. J. Atmos. Environment*, **5**(8), August 1971.
8. Counihan, J., 'Adiabatic atmospheric boundary layers; a review and analysis of data for the period 1880–1972', *Int. J. Atmos. Environment*, **9**(10), October 1975.
9. Cramer, H., *Mathematical Methods of Statistics*, Princeton University Press, 1946.
10. Davenport, A. G., 'The dependence of wind loads on meteorological parameters', *2nd Int. Seminar on Wind Effects on Buildings and Structures, September 1967*, University of Toronto Press, Ottawa.
11. Davenport, A. G. and Isyumov, N., 'The application of the boundary layer wind tunnel to the prediction of wind loading', *2nd Int. Seminar on Wind Effects on Buildings and Structures, September 1967*, University of Toronto Press, Ottawa.
12. Deacon, E. L., 'Gust variation with height up to 150 m', *Quart. J. R. Met. Soc.* **81**, 1955, 562 *et seq.*
13. Deaves, D. and Harris, R. I., *A Mathematical Model of the Structure of Strong Winds*, CIRIA Report No. 76, May 1978.
14. Durst, C. S., 'Windspeeds over short periods of time', *Met. Mag.*, **89**, 1960, 181.
15. Eaton, K. J., Mayne, J. R. and Cook, N. J., 'Wind loads on low-rise buildings—effect of roof geometry', *4th Int. Conf. on Wind Effects on Buildings and Structures, Heathrow 1975*, Cambridge University Press.
16. ESDU, 'Characteristics of windspeed in the lower layers of the atmosphere near the ground: strong winds (neutral atmosphere)' *ESDU Data Item 72026, Amend A & B*, October 1974.
17. ESDU, 'Characteristics of atmospheric turbulence near the ground: Part I, Definitions and general information', *ESDU Data Item 74030, Amend. A*, October 1976.

148

18. ESDU, 'Characteristics of atmospheric turbulence: Part II, Single point data for strong winds (neutral atmosphere)', *ESDU Data Item 74031, Amend. A*, March 1975.
19. ESDU, 'Characteristics of atmospheric turbulence: Part III, Variations in space and time for strong winds (neutral atmosphere)', *ESDU Data Item 75001*, July 1975.
20. GUMBEL, E. J., *Statistical Theory of Extreme Values and some practical applications'*, Applied Mathematics Series 33, US Dept. of Commerce National Bureau of Standards.
21. GUMBEL, E. J., *Statistics of Extremes*, Columbia University Press, New York, 1958.
22. HARDMAN, C. E., HELLIWELL, N. C. and HOPKINS, J. S., 'Extreme Winds over the UK for periods ending 1971', *Climatological Memorandum No. 50A*, HMSO, London, July 1973.
23. HARRIS, R. I., *On the Spectrum of Horizontal Gustiness near the Ground in High Winds*, ERA Report Ef SPI/TI4 (unpublished).
24. HELLIWELL, N. C., 'Wind over London', *Proc. 3rd Int. Symp. on Wind Effects on Buildings and Structures, Tokyo 1971*.
25. H.M.S.O., 'Tables of surface windspeed and direction over the UK', *Meteorological Office Met O. 792*, HMSO, London, 1968.
26. JONES, J. G., 'A unified discrete gust and power spectrum treatment of atmospheric turbulence', *Int. Conf. on Atmospheric Turbulence*, Royal Aeronautical Society, May 1971.
27. JONES, P. M., DE LARRINGA, M. A. B. and WILSON, C. B., 'The urban wind velocity profile', *Int. J. Atmos. Environment*, **5**(2), February 1971.
28. LEIBLEIN, J., *Efficient Methods of Extreme Value Methodology*, NBSIR 74-602, US Dept. of Commerce, October 1974.
29. LOEWE, F., 'The land of storms', *Weather*, **27**(110), 1972.
30. LUDLUM, F., 'Thunderstorms', private communication, 1956.
31. LUMLEY, J. J. and PANOFSKY, H. A., *The Structure of Atmospheric Turbulence*, Interscience monographs & texts in Physics and Astronomy v XII, Wiley, New York, 1964.
32. MANN, N. R., 'Point and interval estimation procedures for the two parameter Weibull and extreme value distributions', *Technometrics*, **10**, 1968, 231–56.
33. MAYNE, J. R., 'The estimation of extreme winds', *J. Indust. Aerodynamics*, **5**(1/2), October 1979.
34. MEYER, P. L., *Introductory Probability and Statistical Applications*, 2nd edn., Addison-Wesley, 1970.
35. NATIONAL ACADEMY OF SCIENCES, *Engineering Aspects of the Tornadoes of 3–4 April 1974'*, Report for the Committee for Natural Disasters, National Research Council, National Academy of Sciences, 2101 Constitution Avenue, Washington DC 20418, USA.
36. OWER, E. and PANKHURST, R. C., *The Measurement of Air Flow*, 5th edn., Pergamon, Oxford, 1977.
37. PANOFSKY, H. A. and PETERSEN, E. L., 'Wind profiles and change of terrain roughness at Risø', *Quart. J. R. Met. Soc.*, **98**(418), October 1972.
38. PASQUILL, F., 'Some aspects of boundary layer description—Presidential address', *Quart. J. R. Met. Soc.*, **98**(417), July 1972.
39. PASQUILL, F., 'Wind structure in the atmospheric boundary layer', Phil. Trans. R. Soc. A, **269**(1199), 1971, 439–56.
40. PENWARDEN, A. D. and WISE, A. F. E., 'Wind environment around buildings', *BRE Report*, HMSO, London, 1975.
41. PRASAD, B. and PANOFSKY, H. A., *'Properties of the Variances of the Meteorological Variable at Round Hill'*, Final Report on Properties of Wind and Temperature at Round Hill, South Dartmouth, Mass. ECOM-0035-F, The Pennsylvania State University, pp. 65–72 (Ch. 7).
42. SHELLARD, H. C., 'The estimation of design windspeeds', *1st Int. Conf. on Wind Effects on Buildings and Structures, Teddington 1963*, HMSO, London.

43. RICE, S. O., 'Mathematical analysis of random noise', *Bull. Tech J.*, **18**, 1944, 282; **19**, 1945, 46.
44. TAYLOR, P. A., 'On wind and shear stress profiles above a change in surface roughness', *Quart. J. R. Met. Soc.*, **95**(403), January 1969.
Numerical Models of Airflow above Lake Ontario, Final Report on IFYGL Sponsored Research Dept. of Transport, Reg. No. H-101-H, 1969.
45. TEUNISSEN, H. W., 'Measurements of planetary boundary layer wind and turbulence characteristics over a small suburban airport', *J. Indust. Aerodynamics*, **4**(1), January 1979.
46. THOM, H. C. S., Remarks attributed to H. C. S. Thom and published in [20].
47. THOM, H. C. S., 'Towards a university climatological extreme wind distribution', *2nd Int. Conf. on Wind Effects on Buildings and Structures, Ottawa, September 1967*, University of Toronto Press.
48. VAN DER HOVEN, I., 'Power spectrum of horizontal windspeed in the frequency range from 0·0007 to 90 Hz', *J. Meteorology*, **14**(160), 1957.
49. VICKERY, B. J. and DAVENPORT, A. G., 'A Comparison of theoretical and experimental determination of the response of elastic structures to turbulent wind', *2nd Int. Conf. on Wind Effects on Buildings and Structures, Ottawa, September 1967*, University of Toronto Press.

Index

Windspeed—*contd.*
  probability density function for, 9
  random fluctuation, 3
  separation into mean and
      fluctuating parts, 4
  simultaneous treatment of two
      components, 13
  spectral density function, and, 57
  time domain, 10–11
  time-invariant, 1

Windspeed—*contd.*
  time-varying, 2, 4, 6
  two points in space, at, 61–5
  variation
    height, with, 120
    space, in, 143–50

Zero plane displacement, 112–13